Building Smart Robots Using ROS

Design, Build, Simulate, Prototype and
Control Smart Robots Using ROS, Machine
Learning and React Native Platform

Robin Tommy
Ajithkumar Narayanan Manaparampil
Rinu Michael

www.bpbonline.com

FIRST EDITION 2022
Copyright © BPB Publications, India
ISBN: 978-93-91392-277

To View Complete
BPB Publications Catalogue
Scan the QR Code:

www.bpbonline.com

Forewords

Dr. Prahlad Vadakkepat
Professor of Robotics and Artificial Intelligence
National University of Singapore

The fourth industrial revolution, Industry 4.0, involves several technology domains, including robotics and artificial intelligence. Robotics and Artificial Intelligence will become omnipresent in near future. As per the World Economy Forum October 2020 Future of Jobs Report, by 2025, 97 million new job roles may emerge that are more adapted to the new division of labour among humans, machines, and algorithms. While 85 million jobs may be displaced by the shift of labour among humans and machines. Exposing young minds to Robotics and Artificial Intelligence is the need of the hour for preparing for such a future. This practical guide to robotics using Robot Operating Systems (ROS) will facilitate that process.

Robotics involves design, dynamics, statics, sensing, actuation, path planning, control, and manipulation. Good understanding of Mathematics and Physics is essential in robotics. Due to the hardware requirements and cost associated with, it is difficult to jumpstart developments in robotics. With the advent of Robot Operating System (ROS), the design, testing and fine tuning of robot operations in virtual worlds has become straight forward. ROS provides rich libraries for hardware abstraction, device drivers, visualizers, message-passing, and management. The Computer

Aided Design (CAD) files for a build space can be imported into ROS and the robots can be made to perform in virtual spaces. The performance improvements can be tested, learned and fine-tuned in virtual spaces. ROS is a powerful environment for learning. Industries use ROS Industrial for fast development of robotic systems. ROS is considered as the Digital Twin for experimenting.

The authors of the book have made use of ROS for imparting the essential domain knowledge and practical implementation steps which are easier for beginners. The chapters on AI and robot design compliment the rest of the chapters. The chapters on Vision and Simultaneous Localization and Mapping (SLAM) are important from practical realization of robot operations in real worlds. The complex SLAM concepts are explained in an easy-to-understand manner. Hope that this book will excite new minds to jumpstart robotics development from a young age. Such minds can lead to newer ideas and concepts paving the way for new start-ups and employment generation.

Roshy John
"The Man who Kickstarted India's Driverless Car Revolution"
- NASSCOM

I have been into developing robots and intelligent systems for various industries for a little over two decades. It has become a passion for a lot of students, professionals and enthusiasts to transform their creative ideas to intelligent automation systems quickly. I find this book as a treasure trove for such people who wants to build robots, embedded and intelligent devices very

very quickly. Most of you who are going to try out fundamental concepts in this book will agree on how concise and clearly he has articulated complex concepts. I would say, Robin Tommy with his years of experience in the domain has created magic with this thought provoking book with plenty of hands-on examples. I find most of the content unique and unseen in other books on Robotics. I am sure that this is going to help students regardless of their age or field of study, to start their journey on creating Quick Prototype Robots using ROS (Robot Operating System), 3D Modelling, 3D Printing and finally sensor based environmental cognition using Machine Learning and Deep Learning.

Vimal Govind MK

Director/ CEO of Genrobotics

Robotics is going to be a major industry in the coming years, by transforming people's life and creating the world a better place, like never seen before; a practical guide to build intelligent robots by Robin Tommy is really capturing the fundamentals of creating robotic machines using native platforms. I believe this book will be of great insight to engineers as well as researchers in Robotics and will add great value in building the industry.

Dedicated to

All the people who believed and pushed us to transform our dream of building a Humanoid Robot, into reality.

About the Author

Robin Tommy is a Rapid Innovation Strategist and Thought leader, who for the past 16 years has been working with customers and partners designing technology solutions using emerging technologies and accelerated prototyping methodologies. He has filed over 90 patents across technologies and design. Robin is a strong advocate for societal and sustainable innovations and has been actively involved in devising products and platforms for the enablement and empowerment of neurodivergent society. He has been awarded with the most coveted 'Distinguished Engineer' by Tata Consultancy Services. He has also been recognized as one among the Top 100 Global Thought leader and Influencer by Thinkers360 for the past two consecutive years. He has won the NASSCOM Engineering and Innovation Excellence Award.

Along with Robin, this book is also co-authored by Rinu Michael and Ajithkumar Manaparambil. Ajithkumar Manaparambil is a robotics developer with expertise in simulation, design and manufacturing of projects pertaining to robotics, automobiles, and special purpose machines. Ajith is currently pursuing his Masters in Robotic Systems Engineering in RWTH Aachen University. Rinu Michael is a technical expert in Artificial Intelligence and Edge Analytics and she is currently heading the TCS Rapid Labs at Amsterdam.

Contributors

We owe our gratitude to many people who have played instrumental role towards the content covered in this book. We appreciate the effort and contribution by:

Reshmi Ravindranathan for her contributions to certain sections of this book and for collaborating with the publishing team.

Jeena Jayaraman, Akash Kaimal and Janu Narayan for their patience in doing multiple rounds of review for the book and helping us to refine the book, to the way it is today.

Jithin L R and Jerin Varghese Thomas, highly specialized in the field of IoT and Robotics, Power management and Human Machine Interface (HMI) design and electronic circuitry.

Gireesh Bandlamudi, an expert in the design and development of Web & Mobile applications and contributed towards integrating mobile applications with ROS.

Anand G, a distinguished robotics engineer, contributed towards embedded systems and robotics.

Georgekutty Johny for sharing his thoughts, knowledge and experiences so generously and honestly, so that the contents will be useful to someone aspiring to build their own humanoid.

About the Reviewer

Dr. Jisha V R has 22 years of experience as a faculty at Department of Electrical Engineering, College of Engineering Trivandrum. Her areas of expertise include Control of Dynamic Systems and Robotics. She has supervised 45 masters' theses and 30 BTech projects and currently guiding 5 research scholars of Kerala Technological university. She has received funding for different projects like Human Operated Exoskeleton, Autonomous Quadcopter, Design of a Biped Robot, Indoor Navigation for visually impaired, Autonomous aerial vehicles etc. She has around 35 publications in international conferences and journals, to her credit.

She received PhD from Department of Aerospace Engineering, IISc Bangalore and completed her UG and PG studies at College of Engineering Trivandrum. She is also officiating as Member, Board of governors, Kerala Technological University; Chair, Strategic Initiatives (Academia), IEEE Kerala Section; Member Board of Studies, BTech Robotics and Automation, Saint Gits College of Engineering. She was also the former Chair, IEEE Robotics and Automation Society, Kerala Section. She currently working as Professor, Department of Electrical Engineering, College of Engineering Trivandrum.

Acknowledgement

"No one can whistle a symphony; it takes a whole orchestra to play it"
H.E. Luccock

The book 'Building Smart Robots Using ROS' is an abridged version of our experiences in creating humanoids ab initio. There were bouts of successes and failures, of uncertainties and confidence, of risks and challenges. There were days when we were lost on how to proceed and a good amount of midnight oil burning to bring the humanoids to completion. But, as they say, what is not possible with teamwork, collaboration and unwavering support.

This book is the outcome of an experience – an experience that was founded on perseverance, hard work and above all, belief. You would not be holding a copy of this book in your hands, if not for a circle of people who pushed us, believed in us, offered their expertise, held us together when things went wrong and so much more. Without them, we would not have been able to create our first humanoid. So, it is imperative to offer our gratitude to them for making this book a reality.

We cannot thank you enough:

K Ananth Krishnan, Anita Nandikar, Dinesh Thampi and Anil Sharma from Tata Consultancy Services for being our constant sources of motivation, guidance, and inspiration and leading by example.

Dr. Jisha V.R., Associate professor, College of Engineering, Trivandrum for reviewing, proofreading, and suggesting technical changes to make the content more relevant and insightful.

Dr. Ranjith S Kumar, Associate professor, College of Engineering, Trivandrum who contributed his technical knowledge and expertise during multiple prototypes and developmental phases.

The Kerala Startup Mission (KSUM), FABLABS and Future Technologies Lab, for providing us the necessary resources and support needed for the fabrication and manufacturing of the humanoid.

IEEE Robotics and Automation Society Kerala Chapter team for all the inspiration and for being a strong enabler in nurturing the future robotic enthusiasts.

The local boat manufacturers at Trivandrum, helping us with knowledge on the various materials that could be used for the outer structure of the robot, and for making us realize that innovations happen in the least probable places.

To the wonderful team at BPB Publishing House for making this book a reality and endless patience in editing the book – Thank you.

The entire TCS Rapid Lab team for being the constant pillars of support and going beyond the call of duty at times.

Our heartfelt gratitude to everyone who have crossed our paths while creating our humanoids, provided suggestions, feedback and criticism.

Our families : for all the selflessness, care and sacrifices.

Preface

The International Organization for Standardization defines a 'service robot' as a robot 'that performs useful tasks for humans or equipment excluding industrial automation applications'. (ISO 8373). Service robots can be categorized to attend to professional and personal purposes. Even though such robots may not belong to the same league as industrial robots in terms of the scale of deployment, they are gradually making their presence felt in several industries.

A personal service robot, as the name suggests, simply refers to bots used for personal use. They are used to assist humans in performing monotonous activities in their day-to-day life. Some of the domestic help that they provide include surveillance and security, elderly and disability assistance, floor cleaning, robotized wheelchairs, remote presence and for general assistance and personal aids.

Professional service robots are normally used outside the home environment. They help in automating commercial processes which are unskilled, time-consuming or repetitive tasks. Service bots can be deployed in business sectors like retail, healthcare, hospitality or even warehouses. The use of robots supports its deployment purpose to improve productivity at minimal costs, build a smart business network and let employees focus on high-value tasks. Additionally, it also helps in enhancing the overall experience of the customers by creating a digital experience through their structural appearance as well as interaction.

Social robots can be regarded as an extension to service robots. Usually, service or industrial bots are not devised to evoke human emotions or react on cues from people. This is what makes social robots distinguishable from the other robots. The social robots have an ability to understand social behavioral patterns, showcase expressions as well as provide appropriate interactions. What makes social bots more appealing is the humanoid embodiment provided to it, which will help in easier engagement with human beings. One area where social robots will make their presence felt in a strong manner is elderly care. It is a known fact that the number of elderly people living alone, with no one to tend to their needs, are increasing on a daily basis. While some of them are not able to take care of themselves, some just need somebody to talk to. This is where social robots come into the picture – as a wellness aid. They will remind them to take walks, medications or basically, just give them company. Social robots can also act as assistive aids, for providing therapy for differently abled children. It is also highly likely that we might be greeted by robots at restaurants, airports, hospitals and other public places. Expanding other technologies like 3D printing, exoskeletons and machine learning acts a synergist in the adoption of robots in many other sectors. One such robot, RADA, developed by TCS for a premium airline in India, is placed at the airport lounge as part of customer and concierge management.

The panorama of domestic robots will be transformed with technologies such as machine learning, computer vision, natural language processing, Big Data and gesture controls. As per the market overview conducted by Mordor Intelligence*, the global service robotics market was valued at USD 23.57 billion in 2020 and is expected to reach USD 212.62 billion by 2026. [**https://www. mordorintelligence.com/industry-reports/service-robotics-market**]

Chapter 1, ROS - Describes the concept and architecture of Robotic Operating System (ROS) along with an introduction to Ubuntu command terminal. Familiarity with the Ubuntu command terminal will help you navigate, execute and monitor the files and data in the ROS system. In the next chapter we will learn how to build and run the basic nodes in ROS.

Chapter 2, Writing Nodes - A brief introduction about the communication type used between nodes in ROS. It describes the various communication methods along with their usage based on the application type. We will learn about nodes and also implement two basic nodes in ROS. In the next chapter we will try to implement and understand ROS nodes in terms of a sensor and an actuator.

Chapter 3, Sensors and Actuators – In this chapter we will be creating a basic program in ROS, based on the concepts covered in the previous chapter. Once the basic node is created, the program is further extended to include actual hardware control. We will get a brief understanding how sensor data is used and shared in the ROS network. We will be using ROS SERIAL package in this chapter which is explained in detail in the next chapter.

Chapter 4, ROS SERIAL – This chapter describes one of the packages used in the previous chapter. The ROS serial package helps the host system communicate to a controller (Arduino) using serial communication. In the next chapter we will learn how to create a web interface for robots that use ROS.

Chapter 5, Web interface - One of the basic problems faced during ROS implementation is the lack of a user interface (for non-ROS users). In this chapter we will learn how to publish and consume data from a ROS network using a web interface. In the next chapter we will learn about a simple two-dimensional simulator that will help us reinforce the concepts learnt in the previous chapters.

Chapter 6, Turtle Sim Simulation - Now as the basics of ROS and the useful packages are already covered, in this chapter we will get an idea about how a robot works within a ROS network. This includes usage of multiple nodes as well as simulation. This chapter explains how to install and use the Turtle sim simulation (2D robot simulation). This chapter will help us understand how all the nodes function together as a single system. In the next chapter we will look into the designing of a simple robot.

Chapter 7, Designing a robot - This chapter teaches how to create a basic differential drive robot in a CAD (Computer Aided Design) software. This model will be later imported into the simulation environment. We will be using a separate software for the simulation environment which is explained in the next chapter.

Chapter 8, Gazebo - This chapter gives an introduction to a 3D simulation environment called Gazebo. All the 3D models (e.g., Robot, Markers) created in the previous chapter will be imported to this environment during the simulation. The Simulation will actually help in testing the real-world scenarios virtually. Some specific tools used for evaluating a robotic arm will be discussed in the next chapter.

Chapter 9, Moveit - This chapter introduces Moveit for manipulator evaluation. Moveit is a software used for motion planning, kinematics and design evaluation. We will be evaluating a robotic arm in this chapter to get a better understanding of Moveit. In the next chapter we will be learning about a visualization tool for robotic systems.

Chapter 10, Rviz - In this chapter, we will be learning about a visualization tool called Rviz: it is a tool used during simulation as well as actual robotic application. This chapter gives an overview regarding the usage and functioning of Rviz.

Chapter 11, Vision - In this chapter we will get a basic introduction about using image processing techniques in ROS. We will learn about a ROS package called cv bridge. This chapter also gives a brief introduction about OpenCV and calibration instructions for Hardware (Camera). In the next chapter we will be learning a particular image processing example which can be used in robotics.

Chapter 12, Aruco Markers - This chapter explains the use of Aruco markers in Robotics. It teaches how to generate markers, how are they read using a camera and the instructions to run a basic program in ROS. We will also be creating a 3D marker model which can be imported to the simulation environment – Gazebo.

Chapter 13, SLAM - In this chapter we will learn the concept and usage of Simultaneous Localization and Mapping. The chapter also describes the ROS packages used for implementing SLAM and a basic example. In the next chapter we will learn how the controls of a robotic system can be ported to mobile devices.

Chapter 14, React Native App - In this chapter we will learn a method to use inputs from apps to run a robotic system. This chapter describes the method to create and run ROS integrated mobile applications.

Chapter 15, Artificial Intelligence - This chapter explains the basics of Artificial Intelligence and Machine Learning. It has a brief description of how to integrate AI and ML packages into the ROS environment along with a sample code.

Code Bundle and Coloured Images

Please follow the link to download the
Code Bundle and the *Coloured Images* of the book:

https://rebrand.ly/5cf3f3

The code bundle for the book is also hosted on GitHub at **https://github.com/bpbpublications/Building-Smart-Robots-Using-ROS**. In case there's an update to the code, it will be updated on the existing GitHub repository.

We have code bundles from our rich catalogue of books and videos available at **https://github.com/bpbpublications**. Check them out!

Errata

We take immense pride in our work at BPB Publications and follow best practices to ensure the accuracy of our content to provide with an indulging reading experience to our subscribers. Our readers are our mirrors, and we use their inputs to reflect and improve upon human errors, if any, that may have occurred during the publishing processes involved. To let us maintain the quality and help us reach out to any readers who might be having difficulties due to any unforeseen errors, please write to us at :

errata@bpbonline.com

Your support, suggestions and feedbacks are highly appreciated by the BPB Publications' Family.

Piracy

If you come across any illegal copies of our works in any form on the internet, we would be grateful if you would provide us with the location address or website name. Please contact us at **business@bpbonline.com** with a link to the material.

If you are interested in becoming an author

If there is a topic that you have expertise in, and you are interested in either writing or contributing to a book, please visit **www.bpbonline.com**. We have worked with thousands of developers and tech professionals, just like you, to help them share their insights with the global tech community. You can make a general application, apply for a specific hot topic that we are recruiting an author for, or submit your own idea.

Reviews

Please leave a review. Once you have read and used this book, why not leave a review on the site that you purchased it from? Potential readers can then see and use your unbiased opinion to make purchase decisions. We at BPB can understand what you think about our products, and our authors can see your feedback on their book. Thank you!

For more information about BPB, please visit **www.bpbonline. com**.

Table of Contents

Introduction

This book is purely based on the experience of the authors in creating a robot from scratch. There were series of designing, fabrication, simulation, and integration of electronic components, etc. that was done, each of them undergoing multiple iterations. The book has been organized such that anyone with minimum prerequisite knowledge would be able to build a robot without any industrial settings.

As per definition, a robot that functions as an intelligent machine, which can be programmed to take actions or make choices based on input from sensors, is an intelligent robot. The degree of intelligence varies from basic robots, which are capable of performing programmable tasks, to advanced robots using artificial intelligence. The core components of a robot can be broadly classified into sensing, actuation, and processing, which vary from the basic to advanced levels based on the type of robot. The component selection and design of the robot are then initiated based on the type of robot and the level of sophistication required for the three core components. Drivers for sensors and actuators and communication between individual programs are common requirements for all robotics projects. Previously, the same drivers and communication programs were re-invented for every robotics project across various institutes and industries. This led to a moderate amount of time being spent on actual robotics research. ROS was developed with the intention to create a common framework that allowed processes to communicate with each other and also provided additional tools for robotics software development. ROS has individual packages and scripts dedicated to commonly used sensors, actuators, drivers, and algorithms, which can be reused across various hardware platforms. Eventually, as the requirements increased, additional third-party simulators were integrated with ROS to provide a complete robotics development platform. Gazebo, an open-source 3D robotics simulator, and RVIZ, a 3D visualization software tool, are two major software tools that have been integrated with ROS.

The initial chapters of this book introduce ROS and its architecture, along with implementations of sample programs for hardware integration. A brief introduction to the simulation and visualization tools in ROS has been provided later, and the final segments of the book focus on the implementation of computer vision, web applications, and artificial intelligence to control the robot.

CHAPTER 1
Robot Operating System

Introduction

Robot Operating System (**ROS** or **ros**) is a meta operating system comprising a flexible set of frameworks for robotic software development.

Efforts and research at the Personal Robotics Program and STAIR at Stanford University brought out the early prototypes of a flexible software for use in robotics. In 2007, *Willow Garage*, a robotics incubator, contributed to developing the basic framework of ROS. The contributions of researchers from around the globe helped develop it into the present day open-source middleware that provides tools, format, platform, and libraries.

ROS provides a framework that makes it easy to share and adapt the code into any system. The system also makes it easy to add features to a pre-existing robot as the architecture is flexible, and the addition or deletion of a node does not crash the entire robotic system.

The problem statements and challenges in robotic applications are affected by several parameters, depending on the instance and environment where the robot is currently active. The software created for a particular instance and environment may not be applicable in other situations even though the underlying task is similar. There is always a demand for more generic and general-purpose software with adequate flexibility for such robotic applications.

Also, general-purpose software is heavily application-dependent. The focus of the work or research shapes the software outcome. A general-purpose software for a robotic arm may not be capable of handling the navigation component. So, there is a constant need for a platform and method for the robotics community to contribute to and share the best in the respective robotics segment.

Structure

We will cover the following topics in this chapter:

- Understanding Ubuntu terminal
- ROS file system
- ROS computation graph level

Objectives

By the end of this chapter, you will be familiar with the what and hows of Ubuntu operating system, i.e., terminal commands, shortcuts for navigation, execution, and monitoring of the files and data in the ROS system.

Understanding Ubuntu terminal

Ubuntu is a Debian based open-source Linux distribution. An Ubuntu terminal is a software package and a command line interface used to run text commands.

Terminal shortcuts on the Ubuntu terminal

Most of the commands used on the ROS terminal are either derived or are the same as those used on Linux terminals. So, one should be aware of the commands used on Ubuntu terminals before going forward with ROS. The following are some of the basic commands used on Ubuntu terminal:

- **~** : home
- **/** : root
- **** : escape for spaces and special characters in run command
- **.filename**: hidden file
- **cd** : The 'cd' command changes/opens the terminal into home directory
- **cd path/** : The above command 'cd' changes/opens the terminal in the directory mentioned by the path
- **cd ..** : Returns to the previous directory
- **./file_name**: Runs executable/binary files or shell script
- **mkdirdirectory_name**: Makes a directory with the name 'directory_name'
- **rmdirdirectory_name** :Removes or deletes the directory with the name 'directory_name'
- **rm -rfdirectory_name**: Removes entire directory with its content
- **Pwd**: Print working directory returns the present working directory
- **Ifconfig**: Returns IP address and MAC address of the device
- **cpfile_pathdestination_path**: Copies file to destination path
- **mv file_name1 file_name2** : Renames file_name 1 to file_name2
- **mv file_pathdestination_path**: Moves file to destination path
- **root**: root is the super user by default. It has access to all commands and files on a Linux/Unix based operating systems like Ubuntu, Mac, Fedora distributions, etc. Linux/ Unix file system hierarchy starts from the root, and it is the

top-level directory of the system where the entire file system resides.

- **sudo**: sudo is an abbreviation for super user do. It helps access and handle files in the root directory.

- **.bashrc**: BASH stands for Bourne Again Shell, and 'rc' stands for 'run commands'. A shell is nothing but an interpreter that can accept commands from a user and run them to perform operations like navigating around file system, running programs, and debugging and interacting with devices.

The **.bashrc** file is called every time when a new terminal is launched. For instance, open the terminal and type the following:

```
sudo nano ~/.bashrc
```

(Nano opens the bashrc file in an editor)

Add the following as the last line of **.bashrc** and save.

```
echo "hi welcome!!! U r working in ROS Desktop"
```

Now, when the terminal is opened, the above statement will be printed whenever the shell is launched.

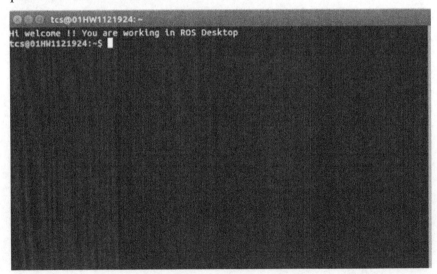

Figure 1.1: Changes due to Bashrc

Hence the **.bashrc** file is a good place to run commands that will help run the command each time the shell is opened.

ROS file system

ROS file system refers to the resources and format in which the required set of programs is found on a system. The following are the terms used in context of ROS and their explanations:

- **Packages**: A package is a combination of nodes, libraries, configuration files, and other relevant scripts that work toward a common functionality. Package is the resource that can be built and released by ROS. For instance, a package created for Lidar has all the relevant nodes, libraries, and files to integrate a Lidar to a robotic system. Packages form the basic unit of programs that can be shared and reused.

- **Meta packages**: Meta packages, unlike packages, don't contain multiple folders, files, and libraries. They contain a single file that group together multiple relevant packages as a single logical package.

- **Package manifests**: Package manifests provide metadata about a package. Metadata refers to information like the name of the package, version, license, dependent libraries, and other meta information to facilitate reusability and compatibility.

- **Repositories**: Repositories represent a group of packages that share a common **Version Control System** (**VCS**). ROS does not consider it mandatory to utilize specific VCS but has put forward certain guidelines to make code sharing easy.

- **Service types**: These define the data structure for request and response for services used in ROS.

- **Message types**: These define the data structure for messages sent in ROS.

ROS computation graph level

One of the features that ROS supports is distributed computing. It inherently uses multiple processes to process data from multiple sources. The peer-to-peer network created by ROS can be explained in a fashion similar to the graph theory. Some of the concepts that should be clear to understand the architecture of ROS enabled systems are as follows:

- **Nodes**: Nodes are the units that perform all the computation. The scripts for nodes can be written in Python and CPP using the client library rospy and roscpp, respectively. A robot may comprise multiple nodes, each dedicated to one task. For instance, one node controls the motors, one node performs path planning, one node controls the camera feed, and so on.

- **Master**: It stores the topic and services registration for ROS nodes. It serves the purpose of name registration and lookup to other components and nodes in the computation graph. It is similar to a DNS server in networking. Nodes communicate their registration information with ROS master and receive information about other registered nodes. Once registered with the master, the nodes can directly communicate with other nodes.

- **Parameter server**: The common or dynamically stable data required by multiple processes in a ROS network can be stored on the parameter server. Multiple nodes can access these values from the parameter server.

- **Messages**: Data is shared between nodes in the form of messages. A message is a data structure comprising typed fields. A message can also include custom nested structure. Examples include primitive message types like float, integer, etc., and nested message structures like CameraInfo message type.

- **Topics**: Topic is the identifier for a message sent in ROS network. A node shares the data by publishing it to a topic. Other nodes in the network can subscribe to the topic to receive the relevant message. Multiple nodes can publish to the same topic, and similarly, multiple nodes can subscribe to the same topic as well. The source of information or sensor data is never affected by the nodes consuming the data. Topics are similar to data bus with a registered name. Any node can connect and publish or subscribe to these buses with the help of the correct message type.

- **Services**: Services are used when there is a need for request/reply type interactions. A message structure is defined for both request and reply messages. A node offers a service under a name. Other nodes can send the request message using the service name and wait for the corresponding reply.

- **Bags**: Bags act as the playback service for the ROS message data. Bags can store sensor data that can be played at a later point in time. This feature is used for testing and developing an algorithm. The data stored in bags can also be used to fine tune the simulations.

Conclusion

In this chapter, we covered the basic commands used on Ubuntu terminal, the ROS file system, and computational graph levels. Most of the concepts and commands specified here will be used in the following chapters.

The next chapter will take you through creating a basic node in ROS, along with integration of hardware.

Key terms

- **ROS packages**: It is a combination of all relevant file systems, including nodes, libraries, configuration files, and other relevant scripts intended for a particular functionality of the robot.

- **ROS messages**: It includes the data sent between nodes with an already defined or custom data structure.

- **ROS topics**: It is an identifier for the data being published on the ROS network. ROS nodes can publish or subscribe messages to an ROS topic.

- **ROS nodes**: ROS nodes are the basic units in the ROS network that perform the computations specific to a functionality of the robot.

CHAPTER 2
Creating a Node

Introduction

Nodes are the subprograms inside an ROS network that can publish a message on a topic, subscribe to a topic, and use services as well. They perform individual functions or multiple functions based on the application and are executable files and generally, reusable pieces of code. They communicate with other nodes in the ROS network and help in distribute and collect the information.

Structure

We will cover the following topics in this chapter:

- ROS listener and publisher
- Sensor-based decision

Objectives

After going through this chapter, you will be able to implement two basic nodes acting as subscriber and publisher. Additionally, you will also be able to implement a sensor-based decision-making node with hardware.

ROS listener and publisher

In the following chapter, an Arduino controller will be used to publish sensor data on a topic and another piece of code to control the motors. Both the sensor and actuator codes will use ROS serial to communicate with the host machine or processor, as shown in *figure 2.1*. The Arduino code in the next chapter publishes to the 'ultrasonic' topic, so a subscriber node 'ultrasonic' will be created in the following section. Similarly, another node that publishes to the 'dcmotorcmd' topic can be created, which will publish the commands for motor control on the 'dcmotorcmd' topic. In the later section, these nodes will be modified so that the motor control will be dependent on the inputs from the ultrasonic sensors.

Figure 2.1: Data flow

Message type to be published/subscribed to: `std_msgs`/`UInt64`

Topic name: ultrasonic

Name of Node: sensorlistener

```
1. #!/usr/bin/env python

2. import rospy

3. from std_msgs.msg import UInt64

4.

5. def callback(data):

6. rospy.loginfo(rospy.get_caller_
   id() + "I heard %s", data.data)

7.

8. def listener():

9. rospy.init_node('sensorlistener', anonymous=True)
```

```
10.
11. rospy.Subscriber("ultrasonic", UInt64, callback)
12.
13.      # spin() simply keeps python from exiting un-
    til this node is stopped
14. rospy.spin()
15.
16. if __name__ == '__main__':
17. listener()
```

The mentioned node subscribes to the topic 'ultrasonic' and creates a log with the following structure:

Caller ID ( ): I heard 'data'.

Similarly, a node must be created to control the motors. The simplest form of this node will publish the '**anti-clockwise**' command to the '**dcmototcmd**' topic. The Arduino program subscribing to the same topic will turn the motor in an anti-clockwise direction. The communication channel from the ROS node to the DC motor has been shown in *figure 2.2*:

Figure 2.2: *Motor control*

The key points to be noted are:

Message type to be published/subscribed to: std_msgs / String

Topic name: dcmotorcmd

Name of Node: talker

```
1.    #!/usr/bin/env python
2.    import rospy
3.    import time
4.    from std_msgs.msg import String
5.
```

```
6.   pub = rospy.Publisher('dcmotorcmd', String, queue_
     size=10)
7.   command = 'anticlockwise'
8.
9.   def dcmd():
10. rospy.init_node('talker', anonymous=True)
11.      rate = rospy.Rate(10) # 10hz
12.      while not rospy.is_shutdown():
13. rospy.loginfo(command)
14. pub.publish(command)
15. rate.sleep()
16.
17. if __name__ == '__main__':
18.      try:
19. dcmd()
20.      except rospy.ROSInterruptException:
21.          pass
```

This code publishes the **'anticlockwise'** command to the **'dcmotorcmd'** topic. The Arduino controlling the motor will subscribe to the **'dcmotorcmd'** topic and receive the relevant command to run the motor.

Sensor-based decision

The next set of modifications will enable the talker node to make decisions based on the inputs from the 'ultrasonic' topic. The talker node will act as a subscriber as well as a publisher.

The key points are:

Message type to be published: std_msgs/String

Message type to be subscribed to: std_msgs/UInt64

Topic names: dcmotorcmd, ultrasonic

Name of Node: talker

```python
1.  #!/usr/bin/env python
2.  import rospy
3.  import time
4.  from std_msgs.msg import String, UInt64
5.
6.  pub = rospy.Publisher('dcmotorcmd', String, queue_
    size=10)
7.  command = 'stop'
8.
9.  def callback(data):
10.     global command
11.     if data <= 30:
12.             command = 'stop'
13. time.sleep(10)
14.             command = 'clockwise'
15. elif data > 30:
16.             command = 'stop'
17. time.sleep(10)
18.             command = 'anticlockwise'
19.
20. def dcmd():
21. rospy.init_node('talker', anonymous=True)
22.     rate = rospy.Rate(10) # 10hz
23. rospy.Subscriber('ultrasonic', UInt64, callback)
24.     while not rospy.is_shutdown():
25. rospy.loginfo(command)
26. pub.publish(command)
27. rate.sleep()
28.
29. if __name__ == '__main__':
30.     try:
```

```
31. dcmd()
32.     except rospy.ROSInterruptException:
33.         pass
```

The modified node subscribes to as well as publishes data. The modified motor control node subscribes to the ultrasonic topic and checks whether the distance from the obstacle is less than or more than 30 cm. Based on the distance from the obstacle, the node publishes clockwise, anticlockwise, and stop commands to the 'dcmotorcmd' topic. These commands are used by the Arduino program to control the motors.

Conclusion

In this chapter, we explored the creation of a subscriber and publisher node.   You were also introduced to nodes that can make decisions based on data received from the sensor. In the next chapter, actual sensors and actuators will be added to the system.

Key terms

- **ROS publisher node**: It is a computation unit or sub program that can publish messages to one or multiple ROS topics.

- **ROS subscriber node**: It is a computation unit or sub program that can receive messages from one or multiple ROS topics.

CHAPTER 3
Integrating Sensors and Actuators

Introduction

This chapter aims to integrate a basic sensor and actuator to an ROS network. Sensors are electronic devices that can measure the physical quantity and deliver output. Sensors, which may be analog or digital, are placed at the input point where they interact with the environment to sense the physical input. This is then converted to electric signals. Common examples where sensors are used include cameras, accelerometer, and microphones.

Actuators are devices that drive a mechanical component once an electric signal is received from the sensor, which causes a physical change by producing heat, force, etc. Examples of actuators are stepper motor, which controls a robotic arm, LED, laser, etc.

Structure

In this chapter, we will cover the following topics:

- Proximity sensor
- DC motor control

Objectives

By the end of this chapter, you will be able to develop a basic program in ROS that publishes and subscribes to sensor data to make relevant decisions for an actuator.

Proximity sensor

In this section, the process of integrating proximity sensors with the robot operating system is explained. The sensor used here is an ultrasonic sensor that will indicate the distance of the obstacle on a topic in the ROS network.

The ultrasonic sensor, as the name suggests, uses ultrasonic waves to measure the distance of the obstacle. The sensor emits and receives the reflected ultrasonic sound waves and measures the distance based on the time gap between emission and detection of sound waves. The sensor works for all physical objects, irrespective of being opaque or transparent. The flow of signal from the sensor to the ROS node is shown in *figure 3.1*.

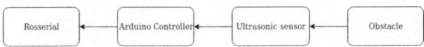

Figure 3.1: *Proximity sensor flow*

The following is the program for an ultrasonic sensor connected to an Arduino board. The program gives the distance of the obstacle as the output.

```
1.   const int trigger = 9;
2.   const int echo = 10;
3.
4.   // defines variables
5.   long duration;
6.   int dist;
7.
8.   void setup() {
9.   pinMode(trigger, OUTPUT); // Sets the trigPin as an
     Output
```

```
10. pinMode(echo, INPUT); // Sets the echoPin as an
    Input
11. Serial.begin(9600); // Starts the serial
    communication
12. }
13.
14. void loop() {
15. // Clears the trigPin
16. digitalWrite(trigger, LOW);
17. delayMicroseconds(2);
18.
19. // Sets the trigPin on HIGH state for 10 micro
    seconds
20. digitalWrite(trigger, HIGH);
21. delayMicroseconds(10);
22. digitalWrite(trigger, LOW);
23.
24. // returns the sound wave travel time in
    microseconds
25. duration = pulseIn(echo, HIGH);//works on pulses
    from 10 microseconds to 3 minutes in length
26.
27. // Getting the distance
28. dist = duration*0.034/2;
29.
30. // Prints the distance on the Serial Monitor
31. Serial.print("The distance of the object is : ");
32. Serial.println(dist);
33. }
```

The Arduino, along with the ultrasonic sensor, can be a part of a ROS network. The Arduino can act as a node and publish the distance of the object on a particular topic. The published value can then be accessed by other nodes comprising of controllers and processors to bring about changes in the current status of the robot.

ROS_LIB libraries should be added to the Arduino IDE before proceeding with the code. Once the library is added, the following code can be executed. It is always helpful to note down the key points to be added.

Message type to be published: std_msgs/UInt64.h

Topic name: ultrasonic

Code:

```
1.  #include <ros.h>

2.  #include <std_msgs/UInt64.h>

3.

4.  ros::NodeHandle nh;

5.  std_msgs::UInt64 distanceros;

6.  ros::Publisher ultrasonic("ultrasonic",
    &distanceros);

7.

8.

9.  const int trigger = 9;

10. const int echo = 10;

11.

12. // defines variables

13. long duration;

14. int dist;

15.

16. void setup() {

17. pinMode(trigger, OUTPUT); // Sets the trigPin as an Output

18. pinMode(echo, INPUT); // Sets the echoPin as an
    Input

19. Serial.begin(9600); // Starts the serial
    communication

20. nh.initNode();
```

```
21. nh.advertise(ultrasonic);
22. }
23.
24. void loop() {
25.
26. // Clears the trigPin
27. digitalWrite(trigger, LOW);
28. delayMicroseconds(2);
29.
30. // Sets the trigPin on HIGH state for 10 micro
    seconds
31. digitalWrite(trigger, HIGH);
32. delayMicroseconds(10);
33. digitalWrite(trigger, LOW);
34.
35. // returns the sound wave travel time in
    microseconds
36. duration = pulseIn(echo, HIGH);//works on pulses
    from 10 microseconds to 3 minutes in length
37.
38. // Getting the distance
39. dist = duration*0.034/2;
40.
41. distanceros.data = dist;
42. ultrasonic.publish(&distanceros);
43. nh.spinOnce();
44. delay(1);
45. }
```

DC motor control

The next step is to integrate DC motor control with ROS. The DC motor mentioned here is without an encoder, i.e., there is no feedback. The approach will be to use Arduino first to control a DC motor. Eventually, the same piece of code can be modified to control the motors over robot operating system.

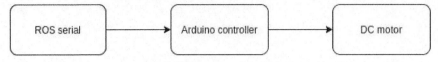

Figure 3.2: DC motor control

This section also gives an insight into how to subscribe to an ROS topic using the Arduino controller. The code snippet used rotates the motor in clockwise and anti-clockwise directions and then stops it. The key points added in Arduino are as follows.

Message type to be published: **std_msgs/String.h**

Topic name: **dcmotorcmd**

```
1.  #include <ros.h>

2.   #include <std_msgs/String.h>

3.

4.  ros::NodeHandlenh;

5.

6.  void motorcmd( conststd_msgs::String& data){

7.    // turn motor

8.    if (data == 'clockwise'){

9.  digitalWrite(in1, HIGH);

10. digitalWrite(in2, LOW);

11.   }

12.   else if (data == 'anticlockwise'){

13.   // now change motor direction

14. digitalWrite(in1, LOW);

15. digitalWrite(in2, HIGH);

16.   }

17.   else if (data == 'stop'){

18.   // now stop

19. digitalWrite(in1, LOW);
```

```
20. digitalWrite(in2, LOW);
21.  }
22. }
23.
24. ros::Subscriber<std_msgs::String> sub("dcmotorcmd",
    &motorcmd );
25.
26. int in1 = 9;
27. int in2 = 8;
28. // motor two
29.
30. void setup()
31. {
32.  // set all the motor control pins to outputs
33.
34. pinMode(in1, OUTPUT);
35. pinMode(in2, OUTPUT);
36. nh.initNode();
37. nh.subscribe(sub);
38.
39. }
40.
41. void loop()
42. {
43. nh.spinOnce();
44. delay(1);
45. }
```

Conclusion

In this chapter, we discussed how sensors and actuators could be connected to ROS nodes on a host computer using ROS serial. The decisions can be made based on input from the sensors. In the next chapter, we will explore the ROS serial package, which was used to connect serial devices to the host computer.

Key terms

- **ROS_LIB library**: It is an Arduino library essential for using an Arduino board as ROS publisher or subscriber.

- **Sensors and actuators**: A sensor is a device that responds to physical stimulus and provides relevant impulse in the required format, and an actuator converts a control signal to the respective mechanical motion.

CHAPTER 4
ROS Serial

Introduction

Ros serial is a protocol used to allow the ROS framework to communicate with embedded hardware. Using this protocol enables communication with a variety of different hardware through ROS topics and services. The Rosserial node should be running on the host machine to communicate with embedded controllers in which the ROS serial node is running. It can be implemented in both Python and CPP.

Structure

We will cover the following topics in this chapter:

- Protocol
- Installing ROS serial

Objectives

This chapter explains how to establish communication between a host system and an Arduino controller using serial communication protocol.

Protocol

The Ros serial communication protocol enables point-to-point communication by sending data in a packet format containing header and tail information to separate data, which allows the ROS platform to send a lot of data at the same time through ROS topics and services.

Packet

A packet consists of a header, payload, and tail. The header has instructions about the data that includes the sync flag, message length, checksum over message length, and the topic ID. The payload consists of the critical data being transmitted. The tail consists of the checksum over topic ID and the message data to detect errors that may have probably occurred during the transmission. The packet format used in Rosserial communication is shown below:

1st Byte - Sync Flag (Value: 0xff)

2nd Byte - Sync Flag / Protocol version

3rd Byte - Message Length (N) - Low Byte

4th Byte- Message Length (N) - High Byte

5th Byte - Checksum over message length

6th Byte - Topic ID - Low Byte

7th Byte - Topic ID - High Byte

x Bytes - Serialized Message Data

Byte x+1 - Checksum over Topic ID and Message Data

Checksum

Checksum over length and data are used to ensure that the data has been received correctly through serial transmission line without any error.

The checksum over message length is calculated using the following equation:

Message Length Checksum = 255 - ((Message Length High Byte +

Message Length Low Byte) % 256)

The checksum over message data is computed using the following equation:

Message Data Checksum = 255 - ((Topic ID Low Byte +Topic ID High Byte + Data byte values) % 256)

The host machine, which is running the ROS platform, must give a request to the Arduino or any embedded controller before the data transmission begins, and the embedded controller responds by giving the topic name and the type of the topic, which is either subscribed to or published by it. The request for the topic uses a topic ID of 0. If the response packet is not received correctly, another request will be sent.

Time synchronization is handled by sending standard_messages: Time in each direction. The embedded device can request the current time from the host machine by sending an empty Time message. This requested time is then used to find the clock offset.

Arduino IDE is an open-source integrated development environment that helps the user easily write code and upload it to the Arduino platform boards. Setting Arduino IDE with Rosserial protocol allows the Arduino to communicate with the ROS platform, which allows researchers to test their products easily. Arduino IDE can be installed from the official website of Arduino. After installing Arduino IDE, you must select the sketchbook folder location where all the Arduino codes and libraries are saved. ROS comes up with an Arduino library called **ros_lib**, which has all the ROS communication libraries built into it.

Installing Ros serial

The following commands are used to install the Rosserial library:

```
sudo apt-get install ros-kinetic- rosserial-arduino
sudo apt-get install ros-kinetic-rosserial
```

Then, the **ros_serial** library needs to be included in the build folder for Arduino. Generally, the sketchbook folder is the location for Arduino where its libraries are found, as shown in *figure 4.1.*

```
cd <sketchbook>/libraries
rosrunrosserial_arduino make_libraries.py.
```

Figure 4.1: Arduino library for ROS serial

After installing this, open the Arduino IDE and check whether ros_ lib is there in example, as shown in figure 4.1.

Conclusion

In this chapter, you were introduced to the basics of how serial devices can be connected to ROS networks. We also covered the concepts of ROS serial package and how to use it. Additionally, we discussed the probable application of ROS serial and how the compatible libraries can be installed in Arduino IDE. The next chapter will provide insights on how to make a web interface to control and monitor the robot.

Key terms

- **ROS serial package**: It provides the necessary libraries, scripts, and file systems to send and receive messages over a serial interface.

- **ROS serial node**: It is a node on the host machine that makes the connection from the serial protocol to the general ROS network.

- **ROS standard messages**: It is a set of ROS primitive data types that are already available in the ROS network for sending messages.

CHAPTER 5

Web Interface

Introduction

'*A picture is worth a thousand words*'. The adage means an image can convey a complex idea more effectively than a description. Then, why not go the extra mile and make an interactive web page with live visualization of the electronic sensor information? The idea is, it would be much easier to understand or debug if a model of robot orienting as per live sensor values can be explored rather than seeing a bunch of numbers indicating the orientation of the robot.

This is where Rosbridge comes in handy. According to *Wiki.ros. org*, "*Rosbridge provides a JSON API to ROS functionality for non-ROS programs. There are a variety of front ends that interface with Rosbridge, including a WebSocket server for web browsers to interact with.*"

Structure

We will cover the following topics in this chapter:

- Installing Rosbridge from a .deb package

- Creating a publisher
- Servo Control
- Creating a Subscriber
- Visualizing sensor

Objectives

After studying this chapter, you will be able to publish and consume the data from a ROS network using a web interface.

Prerequisites

This chapter is meant for those who have basic knowledge in HTML, CSS, and JavaScript. The awareness of these will make it easier to create and animate 3D graphics on a web browser.

Installing Rosbridge

After ROS is installed, Rosbridge can be installed from a **.deb** package.

Use the following command:

```
sudo apt-get install ros-<rosdistro>-rosbridge-suite
```

(Replace rosdistro with ros version ex: roskinetic, rosindigo)

Running Rosbridge

Use the following command to set up the environment for ROS and Rosbridge:

```
source /opt/ros/<rosdistro>/setup.bash
```

To launch Rosbridge and its packages like **rosbridge_server** and **rosapi**, a launch file is included in the install. Use the following command to launch the file:

```
roslaunchrosbridge_serverrosbridge_websocket.launch
```

This will run Rosbridge and create a WebSocket on port 9090 by default. The port can be configured by setting the ~/port param in ROS. A launch file that will run Rosbridge on port 8080 would look like this:

```
1.   <launch>
2.     <include   file="$(find   rosbridge_server)/launch/
     rosbridge_websocket.launch" >
3.   <arg name="port" value="9090"/>
4.   </include>
5.   </launch>
```

Talking to Rosbridge

Now, a basic HTML web page to send and receive calls to Rosbridge can be created. **Roslibjs** is a JavaScript library that handles the communication. For more information on **Roslibjs**, you can click on this link: **http://wiki.ros.org/roslibjs/Tutorials/BasicRosFunctionality**.

First, the required JavaScript files for the application, including EventEmitter2 and Roslibjs, can be imported. Here, Robot Web Tools CDN are used. The files can also be downloaded directly from their respective GitHub repos.

```
1.   <script type="text/javascript" src="http://
     static.robotwebtools.org/EventEmitter2/current/
     eventemitter2.min.js"></script>

2.   <script type="text/javascript" src="http://static.
     robotwebtools.org/roslibjs/current/roslib.min.js"></
     script>
```

The next step is to create an ROS node object to communicate with a Rosbridge v2.0 server. In this example, the script will connect to localhost on the default port of 9090.

```
1.   var ros = new ROSLIB.Ros({
2.   url : 'ws://localhost:9090'
3.     });
4.
5.   ros.on('connection', function() {
6.   console.log('Connected to websocket server.');
7.     });
8.
```

```
9.  ros.on('error', function(error) {
10. console.log('Error connecting to websocket server:
    ', error);
11.  });
12.
13. ros.on('close', function() {
14. console.log('Connection to websocket server
    closed.');
15.  });
```

In the library, it creates a native WebSocket connection to the server, passing messages in the JSON format. This adds a listener for a connection event to the ROS object.

The following two blocks do the same for error and close events. This way, the connection to the Rosbridge server can be monitored.

```
1.  var cmdVel = new ROSLIB.Topic({
2.  ros :ros,
3.  name : '/cmd_vel',
4.  messageType : 'geometry_msgs/Twist'
5.   });
```

A ROSLIB.Topic corresponds to an ROS topic. The topic declares the name and message type and passes it to the ROS object defined while building a ROS node. The topic name and message type are specified while building a node. Node creation was explained in *Chapter 2, Creating a Node,* and *Chapter 3, Integrating Sensors and Actuators.* Topics can be used to subscribe or publish or do both. The browser's developer tools to monitor WebSocket messages can be used.

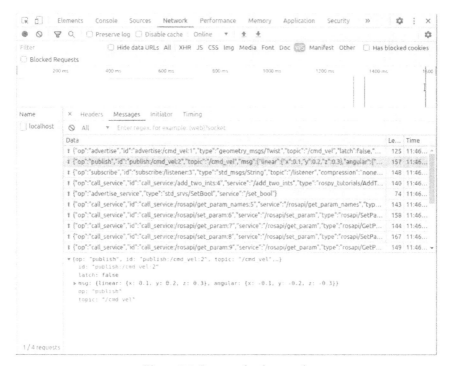

Figure 5.1: *Browser developer tools*

Creating a publisher

The first step is to create a new **ROSLIB.Message** to publish a message. It takes in an object literal that matches the message definition on the ROS system. Nested objects are fine. Once the message is obtained, it can be passed to the **ROSLIB.Topic** to be published.

Controlling hardware

The actuators can be controlled using triggers from the web page. The triggers are initiated using elements like buttons, checkboxes, and sliders. Some of the elements are explained here:

Button actions: For instance, if a specific action like turn on the light for camera or move servo to a defined position from a web page in a click needs to be triggered, publish a message to a specific topic, and the listener on robot gets the message and performs the required action. For this, an HTML element <button> needs to be created, as shown in *figure 5.2.*

Figure 5.2: HTML button

The code snippet to create the buttons is as follows:

```
1.  <button onclick="publish_SetServo(0)">0&deg;</
    button>

2.  <button onclick="publish_SetServo(180)">180&deg;</
    button>
```

Next step would be to link the buttons to appropriate function. This function will execute the respective command on the robot.

```
1.  let ROS_Servo = new ROSLIB.Topic({ros:
    ros,name:"/servo",messageType:"std_msgs/UInt8"});

2.  function publish_SetServo(angle)

3.  {

4.  ROS_Battery.publish(new ROSLIB.Message({data
    :parseInt(angle)}));

5.  }
```

When the button is clicked on, it calls the **publish_SetServo (angle)** function with angle as parameter. Since no validation is done, it is necessary to pass numeric and valid angles as data

We can also consider another example where the headlight of a robot is controlled using <checkbox> HTML element. Refer to *figure 5.3:*

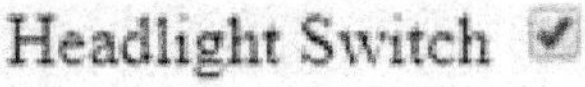

Headlight Switch ✔

Figure 5.3: Checkbox

The following code snippet shows the procedure to add checkbox on the web interface.

```
1.  <input type="checkbox" id="headlightSwitch"
    onchange="sendHeadlightStatus(this.checked)">

2.  let ROS_Headlight = new ROSLIB.Topic({ros:
```

```
       ros,name:"/headlight",messageType:"std_msgs/Bool"});
3.  function sendHeadlightStatus(state)
4.     {
5.     ROS_Headlight.publish(new ROSLIB.Message({data :
       state}));
6.     }
```

The checkbox has two states: checked and unchecked. This Boolean value is published to a topic with name '/headlight'. This is useful in case an ON/OFF switch is needed on the web page.

Servo Control

In the previous example, the servo has been moved to a predefined angle. If the angle of a servo motor needs to be controlled using a potentiometer, the potentiometer equivalent for HTML is range sliders, which can be created as follows.

Servo motor slider

The following code adds a slider on the web interface to control a servo motor on the robot

```
1.  <input type="range" id="servoInput"
    oninput="sendServoAngle(this.value)" min="0"
    max="180" value="90">
```

The event listener for range slider is kept as **'oninput'**, which will call the function every time the slider is moved.

If onchange is used, it will trigger the function call every time the mouse button is released after sliding.

Using **oninput** will consume more bandwidth as compared to **onchange**, but it provides near real-time response. This is essential to fine control servo for experimenting. The same JS function can be reused.

```
1.     let ROS_Servo = new ROSLIB.Topic({ros:
       ros,name:"/servo",messageType:"std_msgs/UInt8"});
2.     function sendServoAngle(angle)
3.     {
```

```
4.   ROS_Servo.publish(new ROSLIB.Message({data
     :parseInt(angle)}));

5.   }
```

Creating a subscriber

To understand the ultrasonic sensor, you must subscribe to the relevant topic.

Visualization of sensor values helps understand the relative position of the obstacles more clearly. In this section, the focus is on how to retrieve data from ROS and display it on the web page.

Visualizing sensor

Visualization can be done in multiple ways, like displaying as plain text, bars, pie charts, graphs, and even 3D models.

Ultrasonic sensor

Consider the example of an ultrasonic sensor. The robot has an ultrasonic sensor, and the requirement is to visualize how the distance changes. Since the code to calculate the distance is written in centimeters, use UInt16 if the distance is more than 255cm; if millimeter precision is needed, it is advised to use Float32.

Any framework or plugin can be used. In this example, the <progress> element will be used. Refer to *figure 5.4*:

Figure 5.4: Progress element

The following is the code snippet to use the <progress> element:

```
1.   <span>Ultrasonic Sensor</span>

2.   <progress id="ultrasonicIndicator" value="0"
     max="255"></progress>

3.

4.   let ROS_Ultrasonic = new ROSLIB.Topic({ros:
```

```
       ros,name:"/ultrasonic",messageType:"std_msgs/UInt8"});
5.    ROS_Ultrasonic.subscribe(function(message) {
6.    document.getElementById("ultrasonicIndicator").
      value=message.data;
7.        });
```

To check whether it is working, a publisher can be used on the same page to check the status. A similar approach can be implemented for battery voltage indication.

Inertial measurement unit

The various parameters of a 3D element can be created and controlled by using the **three.js** javascript library.

For instance, to show the orientation of the robot or orientation of Aruco Marker or Apriltag, x, y, z position in space and the orientation Roll, Pitch, Yaw is required, but this suffers gimbal lock. So, using quaternions will be a good option.

Here's an example for showing orientation of the robot. For this, since the **three.js** Javascript library is being used, this library needs to be included along with **roslib.js**

```
1.  <div id="threeCanvas"></div>:
2.  <script src="three.js"></script>
3.  <script src="OrbitControls.js"></script>
```

Orbit controls is used to move camera in the field, as shown in *figure 5.5*:

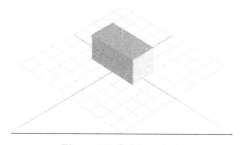

Figure 5.5: Orbit controls

The following is the code snippet for the implementation of Orbit controls:

```
1.
    <script type="text/javascript">
2.
3.          var renderer = new THREE.WebGLRenderer({
    alpha: true });
4.  renderer.setSize(512, 512);
5.  document.getElementById('threeCanvas').appendChild(
    renderer.domElement );
6.          //Initialising three.js scene
7.          var scene = new THREE.Scene();
8.          var hemiLight = new THREE.HemisphereLight(
    0xffffff, 0x0f0e0d, 2);
9.  hemiLight.position.set(5,1,0);
10. scene.add( hemiLight );
11.         //Defining a camera
12.         var camera = new THREE.PerspectiveCamera(
    15, 1, 1, 500 );
13.         var camera = new THREE.PerspectiveCamera(
14.
15.             );
16. camera.position.set(20,10,25);
17.         //Creating Cube
18.         var geometry = new THREE.BoxGeometry( 2, 1, 1 );
19.         var material = new THREE.MeshPhongMaterial(
20.         {
21. color: 0x156289,
22.             emissive: 0x072534,
23.             side: THREE.DoubleSide,
24. flatShading: true
25.         });
26.         var ROBOT = new THREE.Mesh( geometry,
```

```
    material );
27. ROBOT.position.set(0,.5,0)
28. scene.add( ROBOT );
29.         //Create Axis Helper
30. scene.add( newTHREE.AxesHelper( 5 ) );
31.         //Creating Grid for understanding
    reference.
32.         var helper = new THREE.GridHelper( 5,
    10,0xFF0000,0x00FF00 );
33. scene.add( helper );
34.         //Adding orbit control to move camera using mouse
35.         var controls = new THREE.OrbitControls(
    camera,renderer.domElement );
36. controls.target = new THREE.Vector3( 0, 3, 0 );
37. controls.update();
38.         function animate() {
39. requestAnimationFrame( animate );
40. renderer.render( scene, camera );
41.         }
42. animate();
43. </script>
```

This code will create a **three.js** scene and place the camera, light, cube, and other helpers. Instead of cube, the exported CAD model of the robot can be placed. Next, subscribe to the topic to get the orientation and set the orientation of the cube:

```
1.      let ROS_Odometry = new ROSLIB.Topic({ros:
   ros,name:"/odom",messageType:"nav_msgs/Odometry"});
2.   ROS_Odometry.subscribe(function(message) {
3.       var rotation = new THREE.Euler().
   setFromQuaternion({
4.           _x:message.pose.pose.orientation.x,
5.           _y:message.pose.pose.orientation.y,
6.           _z:message.pose.pose.orientation.z,
```

```
7.              _w:message.pose.pose.orientation.w

8.          });

9.    ROBOT.rotation.y = rotation._z;//Currently an setting
      only yaw of the robot.

10.        });
```

Conclusion

This chapter covered how to use HTML, CSS, and JavaScript to create web interface for robots using ROS. The methods of controlling hardware, like servo motors and creating visualizations for sensors like ultrasonic, was briefly introduced. Similarly, other sensors can also be integrated and visualized on a web page. For AprilTags/Aruco Markers*, quaternion orientation can be directly used. The use of Aruco Markers has been described in *Chapter 12, Aruco Markers*. The orientation of Aruco Markers can be extracted in either Euler format or Quaternion notation. This orientation information can then be passed to the web page. The possibilities are limitless once the data is obtained on the web page. In the next chapter, you will learn about a basic 2D simulation package to understand ROS environment and packages.

Key terms

- **Ros bridge**: It is a web socket server that exposes ROS services and functionality using JSON API.

- **Threejs**: It is a JavaScript library that can be used to create and display 3D computer graphics on a web browser.

- **Websocket**: It is a computer communication protocol built over a TCP connection and provides full duplex communication channels.

- **Euler notation**: Notation used to describe the orientation of a rigid body with respect to a fixed co-ordinate system.

- **Quaternion notation**: It is a mathematical notation that describes the orientation and rotation of an object in 3D space.

CHAPTER 6

Turtlesim

Introduction

Turtlesim is a package consisting of basic ROS nodes and a simulation environment. It was made to act as an introductory environment to learn and experiment with ROS and ROS packages. On running turtlesim node, a simulator window consisting of a turtle bot is initiated. The turtle bot has a planar motion and is controlled by using nodes for linear and angular motion. Turtlesim helps get a perspective of how the entire ROS environment works.

Structure

The following topics will be covered in this chapter:

- Understanding nodes and topics
- Setting up Turtlesim

Objectives

After studying this chapter, you will be able to utilize and implement the ROS packages and monitoring methods, including rostopic echo and graph representations.

Understanding nodes and topics

Every package has three basic components: topics, services, and parameters. The turtlesim has two topics: **cmd_vel** and **pose**, which are used to control the position of the turtle bot and to retrieve its current position, respectively. This is shown in *figure 6.1*:

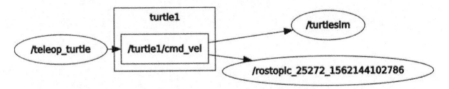

Figure 6.1: Turtlesim nodes and topics

The preceding image shows the nodes and topics active during the simulation. The rectangular blocks indicate the topics, and the oval blocks indicate the nodes. The **/teleop_turtle** node publishes the linear and angular parameters for motion on the **/turtle1/cmd_vel** topic. The **/turtlesim** node subscribes to the **/turtle1/cmd_vel** topic and controls the robot in the simulation based on the instructions received on the topic.

Setting up turtlesim

Once the required ROS version is installed as described in *Chapters 1, Robot Operating System,* and *Chapter 2, Creating a Node,* the next step is to acquire the required packages. Open a terminal and use the following command to install the turtlesim package:

```
sudo apt-get install ros-$(rosversion -d)-turtlesim
```

Replace the rosversion in the above-mentioned command with the current version. In this case, the version used is ROS kinetic.

Once the package is installed, the nodes in *Table 6.1* will be used to start and control the simulation. The **turtlesim_node** starts the simulation, and **turtlesim_teleop_key** is used to control the robots using the arrow keys.

Package	Nodes
Turtlesim	`turtlesim_node`
	`turtlesim_teleop_key`

Table 6.1: Turtlesim package and nodes

How to start turtlesim?

Follow these steps to start turtlesim:

1. Start **roscore** using the command shown in the following figure:

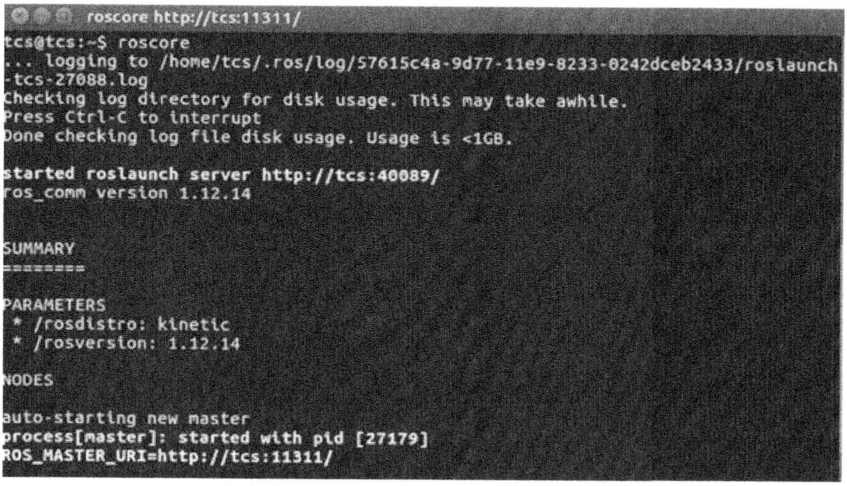

```
roscore http://tcs:11311/
tcs@tcs:~$ roscore
... logging to /home/tcs/.ros/log/57615c4a-9d77-11e9-8233-0242dceb2433/roslaunch
-tcs-27088.log
checking log directory for disk usage. This may take awhile.
Press Ctrl-C to interrupt
Done checking log file disk usage. Usage is <1GB.

started roslaunch server http://tcs:40089/
ros_comm version 1.12.14


SUMMARY
========

PARAMETERS
 * /rosdistro: kinetic
 * /rosversion: 1.12.14

NODES

auto-starting new master
process[master]: started with pid [27179]
ROS_MASTER_URI=http://tcs:11311/
```

Figure 6.2: Roscore terminal

2. Run the **turtlesim_node** by typing the following command:

   ```
   rosrun turtlesim turtlesim_node
   ```

Once the above command is executed on a terminal, turtlesim 2D simulation window opens, as shown here:

Figure 6.3: Turtlesim simulation

Once the turtlesim node starts, a simulation window will pop up with a robot. The next step is to start a node that can be used to control the motion of the robot.

3. Run the **turtle_teleop_key** node to start controlling the robot:

    ```
    rosrun turtlesim turtle_teleop_key
    ```

The **teleop_key** node gives the navigation control of the turtlesim robot to the user, as shown in *figure 6.4*:

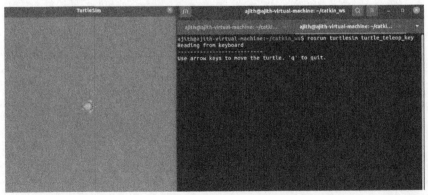

Figure 6.4: Teleop node (Start)

The arrow key, once pressed, will stay active for 1 second, and then it will stop moving the robot. As seen in the above two examples, rosrun is used to run ROS nodes. The syntax for the command is as follows:

```
rosrun<package name><node name>
```

The following image shows the movement of the robot being reflected on the simulator window as per the usage of the arrow keys:

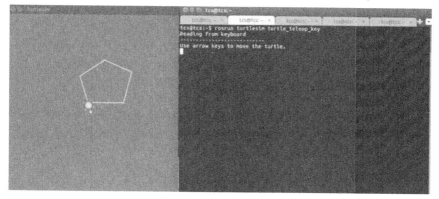

Figure 6.5: *Teleop node (Motion)*

Publishing messages through terminal

Another method for publishing messages on a topic is by using the **rostopic pub** command. This method can help publish test messages on a topic for trial. The syntax for rostopic pub is as follows:

```
rostopic pub <topic name><message type><actual message>
```

The arrow keys used in the previous section publish movement commands based on the usage of the arrow key. The messages can also be published using a command on the terminal with specified location co-ordinates, as shown in *figure 6.6*:

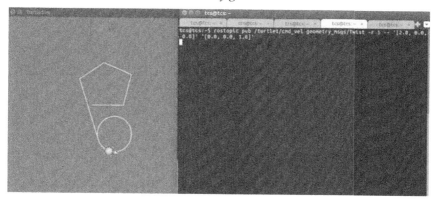

Figure 6.6: *Publishing message using rostopic pub (Turtlesim)*

As seen in the preceding figure, rostopic pub has been used to move the robot in a circle. The command used is as follows:

```
rostopic pub /turtle1/cmd_velgeometry_msgs/Twist -r 1 -
'[2.0, 0. 0, 0.0]' '[0.0, 0.0, 1.0]'
```

The message type is **geometry_msgs / Twist** and is published on the **/turtle1/cmd_vel** topic. The term '-r 1' indicates that the message is published once every second. The next two sections define the linear velocity in x, y, z directions and the angular velocities in x, y, z directions, respectively. The format and the data type for the message is defined by the message type used. ROS has certain types of standard messages. **Geometry_msgs / Twist** is one of the standard message formats. There is also a provision to create and add custom message types to a package. The custom message type can also be included in roslib for Arduino, which can be used by Arduino boards to publish on a particular topic using ROS serial.

Monitoring methods

There are two more useful commands worth mentioning during the turtlesim simulation test: **rostopic echo** and **rqt_graph**. Rostopic echo helps listen to a topic and get the messages on the command terminal. The command used for rostopic echo is as follows:

```
rostopic echo <topic name>
```

The same command has been executed to listen to the **turtle1/cmd_vel** topic.

```
rostopic echo turtle1/cmd_vel
```

This makes the changes in the linear and angular velocities visible on the terminal as shown in the figure 6.7.

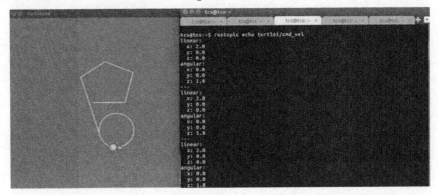

Figure 6.7: Listening to a topic using rostopic echo

The next command is **rqt_graph**, which plots the relation between all the nodes and topic currently present in the package. There are options available to select the currently active nodes and all the present nodes as well as other filtering options.Rqt graph itself is a package installed by default while installing ROS. The command used is the same as rosrun with the package as rqt_graph and the node name as rqt_graph. Once the rqt_graph node is run, the node graph with the nodes and topics of turtlesim package is displayed as shownin *figure 6.8.*

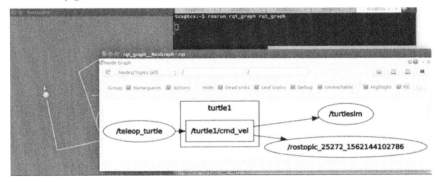

Figure 6.8: Rqt graph generation

Conclusion

This chapter covered the basic implementation of ROS nodes, topics, and environment, and you also understood how prebuilt packages can be used The turtlesim package aids to understand the communication between nodes and the simulation environment. A brief introduction to the monitoring methods, including rostopic echo and graph generation, was also covered.

In the upcoming chapters, we will discuss the creation of nodes and Gazebo models for a custom robot.

Key terms

- **turtlesim package**: It is a lightweight simulator made to teach the basic functionalities of ROS.

- **rostopic echo**: It is a command used to display ROS messages on the terminal.

- **rqt_graph tools**: It is a tool used for visualizing ROS computation graph.

CHAPTER 7
Designing a Robot

Introduction

This chapter will teach you to design a differential drive robot using computer-aided design software. There will be, virtually, two designs for the robot. One of the designs will consist of all the intricate details and parts so that the 3D output can be manufactured. The second design will be a simplified version that can be used for the simulation. The simplified version will have all the physical properties but less detailing.

Structure

The following topics will be covered in this chapter:

- Solidworks
- Unified Robot Description Format (URDF)
- Steps to design a differential drive robot
- URDF conversion
- Visualizing the URDF in gazebo

Objectives

After studying this chapter, you will be able to design a differential drive robot using computer-aided design software.

Solidworks

Solidworks is a proprietary software used for computer-aided design and engineering. It can be installed and is released primarily for windows operating system. For simulating robots in ROS, the parts are needed in Unified Robot Description (URDF) format. Solidworks lacks the ability to export the parts and assemblies in URDF format. Instead, a Solidworks-to-URDF exporter plugin is available on the ROS community, which can be installed and used by Solidworks to export the required URDF files.

URDF

Unified Robot Description Format (URDF) is a format used to describe robot models. The URDF file uses XML representation to describe the parts, joints, sensors, and other physical attributes of the robot. The XML specifications, along with their uses, are as follows:

- **robot**: All the robot properties
- **model**: Kinematic and dynamic properties of the robot
- **link**: Kinematic and dynamic properties of the individual links for the robot
- **joint**: Joint property and types for all the joints between the corresponding links
- **transmission**: Actuator properties that govern the movement of joints
- **sensor**: Properties and attributes of the sensors
- **gazebo**: Properties required for simulation in gazebo, like friction
- **model state**: State of the model at a specific time

Steps to design

The design can be broadly divided into two steps consisting of part modeling and assembly. The design is then converted into URDF using the Solidwork-to-URDF plugin. Part modeling indicates the individual parts that combine to form the entire robot. In the following example, part modeling will consist of two segments.

Part modeling

The following sections will provide further insights into the steps in the part modeling.

Designing the Frame

The frame design includes the platform for the mounting sensor, the brackets for the wheels, and the castor wheel representation. The castor wheel has been simplified into a hemisphere that will slide against the ground plane in the Gazebo world. The bottom view of the Frame Design is shown in *figure 7.1*:

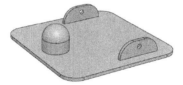

Figure 7.1: Frame design- bottom view

The top view of the platform is as shown in the *figure 7.2*:

Figure 7.2: Frame design - top view

The frame is modeled as three separate parts and combined in the assembly workbench of solidworks. The detailed steps for modeling the parts are stated here:

1. Open solidworks and click on **File** | **New** | **Part**, as shown here:

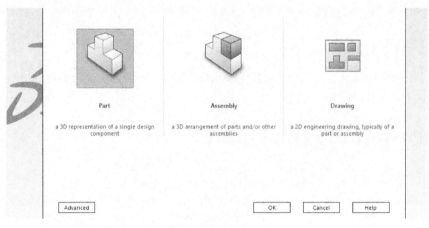

Figure 7.3: New part

2. Select the top plane.

Figure 7.4: Top plane selection

3. Click on **Sketch**.

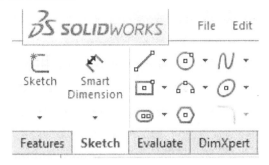

Figure 7.5: Sketch tab

4. Draw a frame profile (Square).

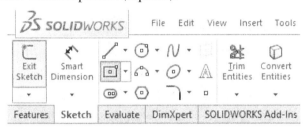

Figure 7.6: Center rectangle

5. Use smart dimensions and provide the appropriate dimensions.

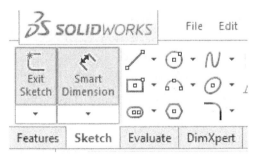

Figure 7.7: Smart dimension

6. Once smart dimension is selected, enter the appropriate width and height.

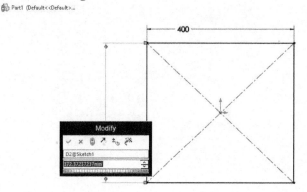

Figure 7.8: Dimension

7. Exit the sketch.

Figure 7.9: Exit sketch

8. Select the sketch, click on extrude, and give the thickness.

Figure 7.10: Extrude option

9. Click on fillet, select the corners, provide the radius, and click on **ok**.

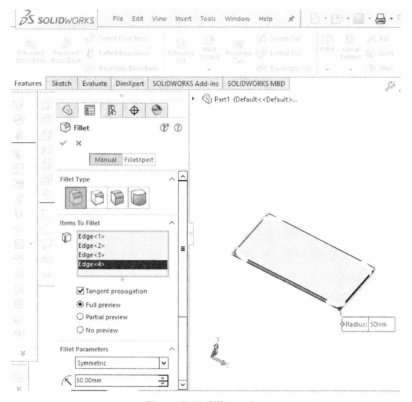

Figure 7.11: Fillet option

10. Select the front plane, enter the sketch, and draw a square (representing the bracket). Use smart dimension and provide the required length.

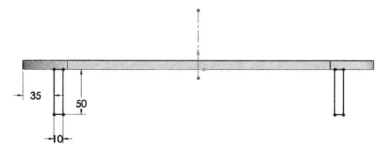

Figure 7.12: Sketch for bracket

11. Draw a construction line at the center.

12. Use the mirror option to select and replicate the same sketch depicted in step 10 and exit the sketch.

Figure 7.13: Mirror option

13. Extrude the sketch drawn with appropriate length.

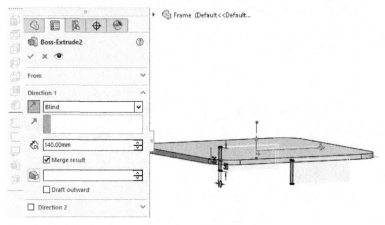

Figure 7.14: Extruding the bracket

14. Use fillet on the brackets.

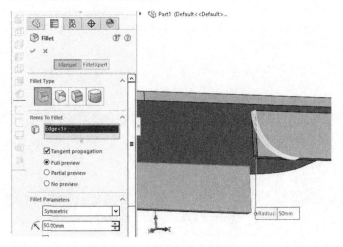

Figure 7.15: Fillet for bracket corners

15. Select the bracket surface and click on sketch.

Figure 7.16: *Sketch on bracket surface*

16. Draw a circle at the center (mounting for the wheel shaft) and exit the sketch.

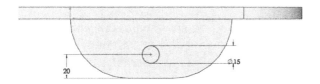

Figure 7.17: *Shaft mounting hole*

17. Use extruded cut to create the hole.

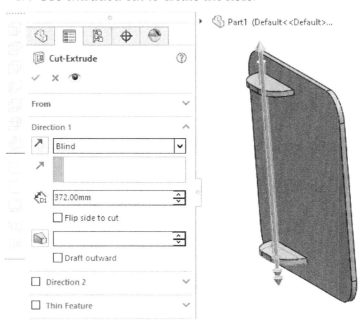

Figure 7.18: *Cut extrude*

18. Save the file as **Frame**.

Designing the wheels

Excluding the castor, two drive motors are placed in the robot. A single wheel can be designed and symmetrically placed on the frame.

Figure 7.19: Wheel design

Once the frame is designed, the next part consisting of two identical wheels is designed. As the wheels are identical, a single wheel is designed and then replicated in the assembly. The steps to design the wheel are stated here:

1. Open Solidworks and click on **File | New | Part**.

2. Select the right plane.

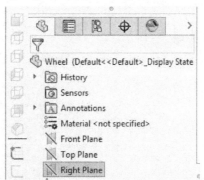

Figure 7.20: Select the right plane

3. Click on sketch.

4. Draw a frame profile (Circle).

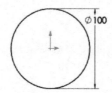

Figure 7.21: Sketch the profile

5. Use smart dimensions and provide the appropriate dimensions (Radius : 100 mm).

6. Then, exit the sketch.

7. Click on extrude and give the thickness.

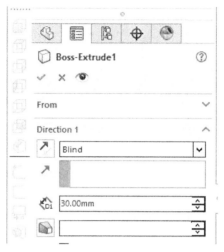

Figure 7.22: Apply wheel thickness by extrusion

8. Click on **Fillet**, select the corners, provide the radius, and click on **ok**.

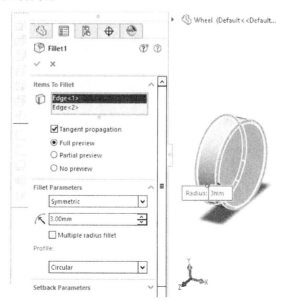

Figure 7.23: Fillet (wheel edge)

9. Then, select the front surface, enter the sketch, and draw a pattern.

Figure 7.24: Sketch on front surface

10. Use smart dimension and provide the required length.

11. Exit Sketch.

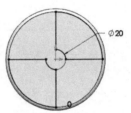

Figure 7.25: Wheel pattern

12. Now, cut extrude the sketch drawn with appropriate length.

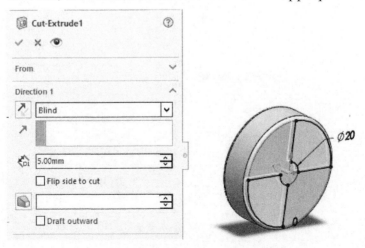

Figure 7.26: Cut extrude the pattern

13. Then, select the rear surface and enter the sketch.

14. Draw a circle at the center (wheel shaft) and exit the sketch.

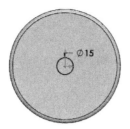

Figure 7.27: *Shaft profile*

15. Use extrude to create the shaft.

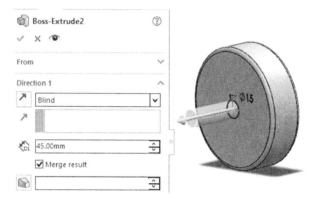

Figure 7.28: *Extrude (shaft)*

16. Fill the haft edge.

17. Save the file as **wheel**.

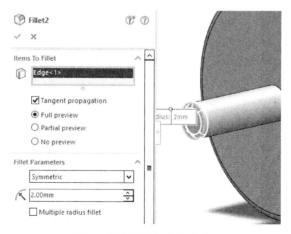

Figure 7.29: *Fillet at shaft edge*

Assembly

Assembly is the process in which the parts created in the previous sections are assembled with the appropriate constraints. Constraints define the degree of freedom of that particular part of the assembly. In assembly, the constraints are applied using the mate option.

The procedure to build the assembly is as follows:

1. Open Solidworks and select **File** | **New** | **Assembly**.

2. After the assembly window opens, a panel with the title Begin Assembly is visible. Click on **Browse** and select the frame that was created.

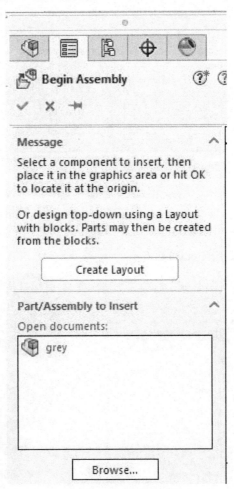

Figure 7.30: Begin assembly

3. Insert the frame and click on **ok**.

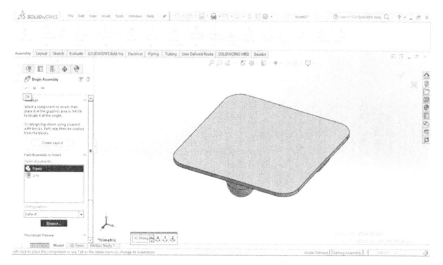

Figure 7.31: Frame in assembly work bench

4. Click on the `Insert Components` tab.

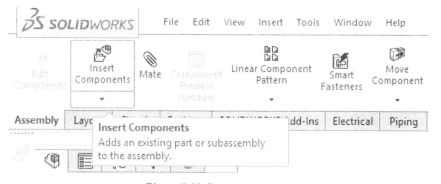

Figure 7.32: Insert component

5. Click on **Browse** and select the wheel that was created in the previous section.

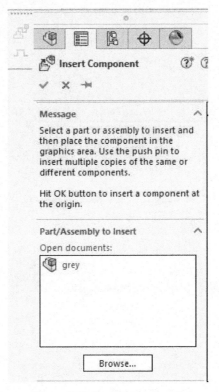

Figure 7.33: Browse components

6. Once the new component appears in the window, there is a provision to rotate the objects. The components can be rotated and aligned to mating end.

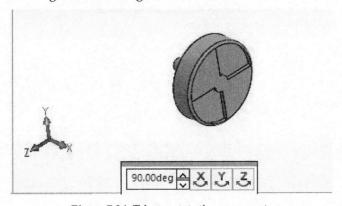

Figure 7.34: Tabs to rotate the components

7. After the component is aligned, click on the **Mate** tab.

Figure 7.35: Mate to apply constraints

8. Now, select the outer surface of the shaft on the wheel and the inner surface of circular pocket on the frame.

Figure 7.36: Mate selections

9. Click on **Concentric** and select **ok**.

Figure 7.37: Concentric mate

10. Select the edges on the shaft and the pocket and use the mate coincident.

Figure 7.38: Select the edges (Mate selection)

11. Select the coincident and click on **ok**.

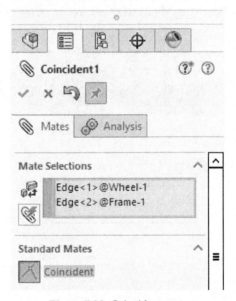

Figure 7.39: Coincident mate

12. Repeat the same procedure for the right wheel to complete the assembly. Finally, save the assembly file.

Figure 7.40: Full robot assembly

URDF conversion

In this section, the URDF exporter is used to convert the previously made assembly into a URDF file. The joint links, names, and types should be specified in the panel before exporting the URDF. The URDF exporter will create a package with the required directories, launch files, URDF, and the STL files. This directory can be directly used to visualize the robot in Gazebo. The export URDF option is available in Solidworks only if the plugin has already been installed.

The previously built robot assembly now needs to be converted into URDF. The following steps state the procedure for Solidworks to URDF conversion:

1. After the assembly is saved, click on **File** | **Export as URDF**.

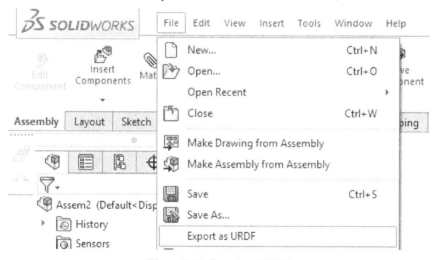

Figure 7.41: Export as URDF

2. A new window will pop up with the information about the base link.

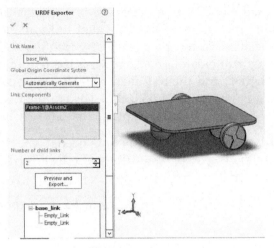

Figure 7.42: Base link

3. Click on the link components section and select the frame. Then, go to the number of child links tab and select two. The wheels form the two-child links.

4. Once the number of child links are created, two empty links will be generated below the base link. Click on one of the empty links to fill in details about the child link.

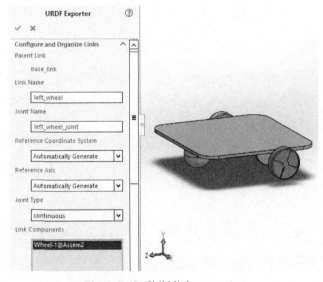

Figure 7.43: Child link parameters

5. Fill in the link name and joint name, as shown in the above figure. Select the joint type as continuous. Then, click on the link components tab and select the left wheel. Then, scroll down and click on the second empty link and fill in the details for the right wheel as shown in *figure 7.43*.

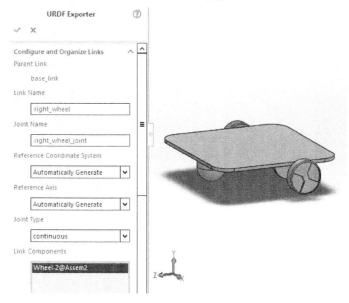

Figure 7.44: *Right wheel (Child link)*

6. Once both the links are filled in, click on preview and export as shown in *figure 7.44*.

Figure 7.45: *Preview and export*

7. Once preview and export is clicked on, a summary with all the relevant information will be formed. Then, click on **Next** and **Finish**.

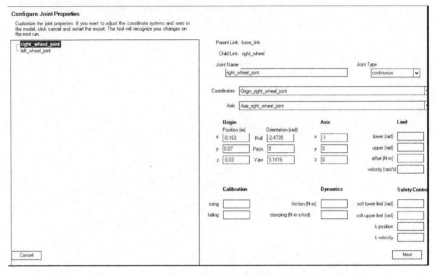

Figure 7.46: Preview

8. Select a location to save the URDF and click on **Save**.

Visualize the URDF in Gazebo

The URDF generated by the Solidworks-to-URDF plugin is already arranged in directories compatible with ROS. The name specified for the URDF folder is 'grey' in the above example. The 'grey' folder has other subfolders like config, launch, meshes, texture, URDF, and two other files called cmakelist and 'package.xml'. Some modifications are required to visualize the robot in gazebo, which are as follows:

1. Go to the '**package.xml**' file and replace the mail ID in the following line with an existing mail ID:

    1.   `<author>me</author>`

    2. `<maintainer email="me2email.com" />`

2. Then, go to the launch folder, open the **gazebo.launch** file, and make the following change:

    1. `<node`

    2.   `name="spawn_model"`

```
3.  pkg="gazebo_ros"
4.      type="spawn_model"
5.  args="-file $(find grey)/robots/grey.urdf -urdf
    -model grey"
6.      output="screen" />
```

3. Replace the word 'robots' with 'urdf'. (The URDF exporter gives a default folder name instead of urdf). The corrected segment will look as follows:

```
1.  <node
2.      name="spawn_model"
3.  pkg="gazebo_ros"
4.      type="spawn_model"
5.  args="-file $(find grey)/urdf/grey.urdf -urdf
    -model grey"
6.      output="screen" />
```

4. Copy this folder to a package in **catkin_ws** once the required changes are made. For the purpose of demonstration, the folder is copied to the package named '**book_gazebo**'.

Figure 7.47: Add urdf to a package

5. Now, open a terminal and build the package where the '**grey**' folder is placed. Use the following command to build the package:

```
catkin_make
```

6. Now, start the launch file using the following command:
```
roslaunchbook_gazebogazebo.launch
```

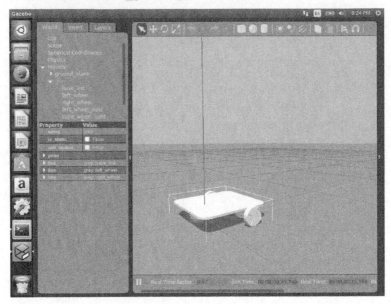

Figure 7.48: URDF model in simulation environment (Gazebo)

Conclusion

In this chapter, you understood the procedure to create a 3D model for a custom differential drive robot. The same concept can be further extended toward robotic arms. We also briefly discussed the conversion of **computer-aided design (CAD)** models to **unified robot description format (URDF)**. These models can then be imported to the simulation environment and tested. In the next chapter, you will be introduced to a simulation environment for robots that can be used along with ROS.

Key terms

- **Solidworks part and assembly**: It refers to individual components of a design (part) that work in unison to form a mechanism or device (assembly).

- **URDF format**: Unified Robot Description Format is an XML format for representing a robot model.

- **Solidworks to URDF plugin**: It is an external plugin for Solidworks that converts Solidworks models to URDF format.

CHAPTER 8
Gazebo

Introduction

Gazebo is an open-source 3D robotics simulator. Gazebo provides a simulation environment with actual physics parameters that enable us to create a virtual simulation of a robot. Gazebo puts to use the OpenD Physics simulator for rendering real-world physics.

Structure

In this chapter, the following topics will be covered:

- Why simulations
- Setting up gazebo
- Designing a world in gazebo
- Adding a robot model to gazebo
- Gazebo plugins
- Launching the gazebo model

Objectives

By the end of this chapter, you will be able to create different elements and integrate them with ROS URDF models using basic functionalities in gazebo. You will also be able to attach and read sensor and motor inputs in a Gazebo simulation.

Why Simulations?

Simulations are efficient when an algorithm for the functioning of a robot is to be developed. The current simulation tools are so powerful that often, the code can be directly uploaded to the robot with minimal modification. Simulations also help reduce the time taken for testing and implementation of the code, and they provide a cost-effective way to learn about the various functionalities of a robot and to test the codes used in them before using an actual robot.

A simulator aims to provide a 3D virtual environment of the robot and its surroundings. A 3D model of the robot is created and its environment is designed and displayed in the simulator. The robot can also have virtual models of the various sensors added. This enables us to check the values coming from the sensors and develop algorithms accordingly. Simulations are widely used for testing different robotic algorithms like SLAM before deploying them on the robot.

Setting up gazebo

Gazebo gets automatically installed if the full version of ROS desktop is downloaded. Else, it must be downloaded by running the following command:

```
sudo apt install ros-kinetic-gazebo-ros
```

Once it is installed, run the following command to open Gazebo:

```
gazebo
```

Note that if gazebo is being run for the first time, it may take some time to load the environment as several models have to be downloaded before they are rendered.

Once gazebo is loaded, you can see that one plane is present in the planes tab, known as the ground plane, as shown in *figure 8.1*. This is the base where the robot and its environment are set up.

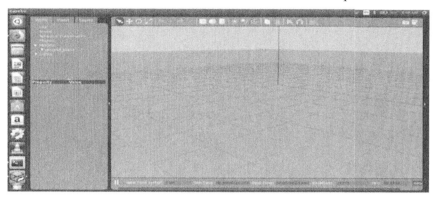

Figure 8.1: Gazebo Empty World

Designing a world in gazebo

To design a model in gazebo, a 3D model of the elements in the environment is needed; pre-installed models in gazebo can also be used.

To design a virtual building environment for a robot, go to **Edit** | **Building Editor**. The following window will appear:

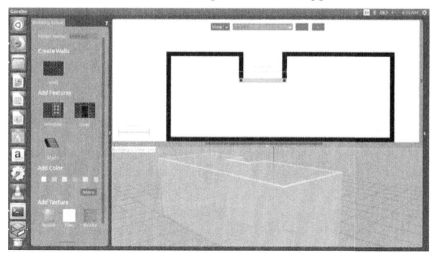

Figure 8.2: Designing a world in gazebo

Now, click on the style of walls required and drag it across the top screen to render it. Elements like walls can be put up in the environment. After designing a building, exit the building editor and save the world configurations by going to **File** | **Save WorldAs** and choosing the required location to save it in.

Adding a robot model to gazebo

To add a robot model to gazebo, ensure that every link has the inertial element added to it. Now, a gazebo reference can be added to every link in the robot.

Material parameters

To define the color and texture of a link in gazebo, first define or import that color or texture in the URDF file. Then, add the **<material>** tag with the color to give that color or texture to the link, as shown in the following code:

```
1.   <material name="Red">
2.   <colorrgba ="1.0  0.0  0.0  1.0"/>
3.   </material>
4.   <gazebo reference="base_link">
5.   <material>Gazebo/Red</material>
6.   </gazebo>
```

Gazebo plugins

Plugins are used in gazebo to simulate sensors and actuators in the robot. There are plugins for various sensors like LIDARS, cameras, distance sensors, etc. There are also plugins for actuators used in the movement of the robot. For a differential drive robot, the **differential_drive_robot** plugin provides a method to send the **cmd_vel** velocities provided by ROS to the rpm of the wheels in the simulation.

Model plugins

Model plugins are used when a particular robot model needs to be imported to the URDF code. To add the differential drive robot plugin to gazebo, edit the URDF to add the following code:

```
1.  <gazebo>
2.  <plugin name="differential_drive_controller"
    filename="libdiffdrive_plugin.so">
3.         ... plugin parameters ...
4.  </plugin>
5.  </gazebo>
```

Sensor plugins

Sensors can also be represented using various plugins. The Hokuyo Controller Plugin enables adding a Hokuyo LIDAR to the gazebo model. The following code adds the LIDAR to the robot:

```
1.  <gazebo reference="hokuyo_link">
2.  <sensor type="gpu_ray" name="head_hokuyo_sensor">
3.  <pose>0 0 0 0 0 0</pose>
4.  <visualize>false</visualize>
5.  <update_rate>40</update_rate>
6.  <ray>
7.  <scan>
8.  <horizontal>
9.  <samples>720</samples>
10. <resolution>1</resolution>
11. <min_angle>-1.570796</min_angle>
12. <max_angle>1.570796</max_angle>
13. </horizontal>
14. </scan>
15. <range>
16. <min>0.10</min>
17. <max>30.0</max>
18. <resolution>0.01</resolution>
19. </range>
20. </ray>
21. <plugin name="gazebo_ros_head_hokuyo_controller"
```

```
      filename="libgazebo_ros_gpu_laser.so">
22.  <topicName>/myrobot/scan</topicName>
23.  <frameName>hokuyo_link</frameName>
24.  </plugin>
25.  </sensor>
26.  </gazebo>
```

Some of the parameters are explained as follows:

- **\<visualize\>**: This enables us to visualize the laser ray. While turned on, various laser rays can be seen being emitted from the robot. This can be useful for seeing what the LIDAR is seeing.

- **\<samples\>**: Defines the number of samples to be taken in a 360-degree rotation.

- **\<topicName\>**: Defines the topic in which the laser readings should be published.

- **\<frameName\>**: Defines the TF to which the laser data should be added.

Launching the gazebo model

To launch the gazebo model, **gazebo_ros** must be launched from the launch file. Update the launch file as follows:

```
1.   <launch>
2.   <arg name="paused" default="false"/>
3.   <arg name="use_sim_time" default="true"/>
4.   <arg name="gui" default="true"/>
5.   <arg name="headless" default="false"/>
6.   <arg name="debug" default="false"/>
7.   <include file="$(find gazebo_ros)/launch/empty_world.
     launch">
8.   <arg name="debug" value="$(arg debug)" />
9.   <arg name="gui" value="$(arggui)" />
10.  <arg name="paused" value="$(arg paused)"/>
```

```
11.  <arg name="use_sim_time" value="$(arguse_sim_
     time)"/>

12.  <arg name="headless" value="$(arg headless)"/>

13.  </include>

14.  <param name="robot_description" command="$(find
     xacro)/xacro.py '$(find my_robot)/urdf/my_robot.
     xacro'" />

15.  <node name="urdf_spawner" pkg="gazebo_ros"
     type="spawn_model" respawn="false" output="screen"

16.  args="-urdf -model diff_wheeled_robot -param robot_
     description"/>

17.  </launch>
```

Run the launch file and the robot would have been loaded in gazebo.

Conclusion

In this chapter, we discussed the need for a simulation software and the basics of using gazebo. The creation of different elements in gazebo and the methods for integrating it with our ROS URDF was explained, and the methods for attaching and reading sensor and motor inputs in a gazebo simulation were also mentioned.

In the next chapter, you will get a brief introduction to RVIZ and 3D visualization.

Key terms

- **Gazebo world and models**: Gazebo world refers to a simulated world with a database of models of basic objects.

- **Gazebo ros packages**: It provides the necessary interface and file systems to simulate a robot in gazebo world using ROS. **Gazebo plugins**: It is a piece of code compiled as a shared library and inserted into simulation, which can access all the functionalities of Gazebo.

- **Gazebo** launch file: It provides a convenient way to start multiple nodes and master to simulate the robot in Gazebo.

CHAPTER 9
RVIZ

Introduction

RVIZ is a powerful robotics visualization tool. It helps get a remote person view of the robot. It can be used for visualizing the various topics that are published in ROS. RVIZ can be used for visualizing URDF, laser scanned data, maps published, and so on. It comes pre-installed when ROS is downloaded.

Structure

In this chapter, the following topics will be covered:

- Launching RVIZ
- Adding elements to RVIZ

Objectives

After studying this chapter, you will be able to visualize data using RVIZ from various ROS topics.

Launching RVIZ

Run the following command to launch RVIZ:

```
rosrun rviz
```

A blank window, as shown in *figure 9.1*, opens:

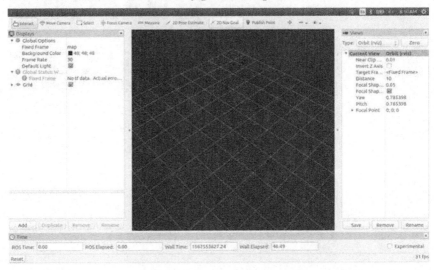

Figure 9.1: Blank RVIZ window

Adding elements to RVIZ

RVIZ consists of different visualization elements called displays. These elements can be added to RVIZ using the '**Add**' option.

Figure 9.2: RVIZ visualization elements

The display includes multiple visualization data. RVIZ does not help simulate a robot but helps in the visualization of the robot that is being simulated in gazebo. The display elements can be selected based on the display type or based on the topic. Laser scan, marker, point cloud, map, and odometry are examples of elements that can be displayed.

Visualizing the URDF of a robot

To visualize the URDF of a robot, the URDF needs to be transmitted as a robot state topic. The tf broadcaster should be transmitting the states of various links and joints in the body. Add the following lines to the launch file:

```
1.  <param name="robot_description" command="$(find
    xacro)/xacro.py '$(find my_robot)/urdf/robot.xacro'"
    />

2.  <include file="$(find my_robot)/launch/empty_world.
    launch">

3.  </include>
```

```
4.  <node name="joint_state_publisher" pkg="joint_
    state_publisher" type="joint_state_publisher" ></
    node>

5.  <!-- start robot state publisher -->

6.  <node pkg="robot_state_publisher" type="robot_
    state_publisher" name="robot_state_publisher"
    output="screen" >

7.  <param name="publish_frequency" type="double"
    value="50.0" />

8.  </node>
```

The following parameters are present in the code:

- **robot_description parameter**: This parameter loads the URDF of the robot into a parameter file. This parameter can then be transmitted to the various transform publishers.

- **Publish_frequency**: The parameter determines the rate at which the joint state publisher and robot state publisher publish the topics; value is given in milliseconds.

The following nodes are run in the preceding code:

- **joint_state_publisher**: This node takes the URDF of the robot and publishes the transforms between the various joints in the URDF.

- **robot_state_publisher**: This node generates the transform between the robot body and the plane on which it is sitting.

Once the corresponding changes are made in the launch file, open RVIZ using the following command:

rosrunrvizrviz.

To visualize the robot, base frame should be added to the RVIZ window. To add a base frame, click on the fixed frame option under global status and select the base frame of the robot. If it is a mobile robot, select the "**odom**" option as the fixed frame.

RVIZ configuration

RVIZ opens with a default configuration file. The default window requires the user to specify the fixed frame and elements to display.

Once the elements are selected, the configuration can be saved. This configuration file can be used to launch the RVIZ window for future instances without manually selecting the elements.

Click on **File** | **Save Config** to save the configuration.

Use the following command to launch RVIZ with the configuration file:

```
rosrunrvizrviz -d ~/.rviz/myconfig.rviz
```

where myconfig is the name of the saved configuration file.

Adding RVIZ to a launch file

Add the following lines to RVIZ to start RVIZ with launch file:

```
1.   <launch>

2.   <node type="rviz" name="rviz" pkg="rviz" args="-d
     $(find package_name)/rviz/config_file.rviz" />

3.   </launch>
```

The actual implementation of RVIZ will be demonstrated in the next chapter.

Conclusion

In this chapter, we covered launching a robot model in RVIZ. You also got a brief introduction to the powerful visualization capabilities of this tool.

In the next chapter, you will be introduced to a motion planning framework, MoveIt.

Key terms

- **RVIZ elements**: It refers to the various functionalities within the RVIZ user interface.

- **RVIZ configuration**: It helps save a particular RVIZ layout required for a specific robot.

CHAPTER 10
MoveIt

Introduction

MoveIt is a tool used for mobile manipulation. It combines functionalities like perception, kinematics, motion planning, trajectory planning, and execution tasks in robotics. The platform is built with an easy-to-configure feature, which means it can integrate with any custom robotic arm having different configurations. It also provides high performance and flexibility to develop and use the mobile manipulation capabilities of a robotic arm. RVIZ visualization window in ROS provides a MoveIt plugin so that it will be easy for the developer to create a MoveIt package for any custom robot they are building. This chapter helps you gain a basic understanding of how to make a MoveIt package for the custom robotic arm. MoveIt can be installed using the following command:

```
sudo apt-get install ros-kinetic-moveit
```

Structure

The following topics will be covered in this chapter:

- Create the MoveIt package for a custom robot
- Defining planning groups

- Defining robot pose
- Defining end effector
- Defining passive joints
- Setting up 3D perception sensors
- Simulating with gazebo
- Setting up ROS controllers
- Getting MoveIt configuration files
- Planning and execution for the robotic arm

Objectives

This chapter will help you understand the procedure to create a MoveIt package for a custom robotic arm.

Creating MoveIt package for a custom robotic arm

MoveIt setup assistant is used to create a MoveIt package for the path planning of a custom robotic arm. The robotic arm being used is Uarm. MoveIt setup assistant is a graphical user interface used to configure any custom robot with MoveIt.

The following command is used to start MoveIt setup assistant:

`roslaunchmoveit_setup_assistantsetup_assistant.launch`

Once the above command is executed, the moveit setup assistant window appears as shown in *figure 10.1.*

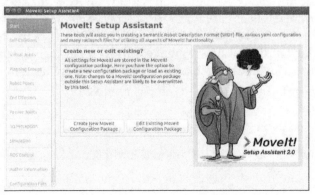

Figure 10.1: *MoveIt setup assistant window*

The **Unified Robot Description Format** (**URDF**) file for the robotic arm needs to be uploaded for creating a new MoveIt configuration package. URDF is an **Extensible Markup Language** (**XML**) format that describes all the elements of a robotic arm. It gives information about each link in the robotic arm, such as the length and mass of each link, along with the type of the joint in the robotic arm, the material used, and so on.

If the URDF file is successfully loaded, the robot model in the MoveIt setup assistant window is as shown here:

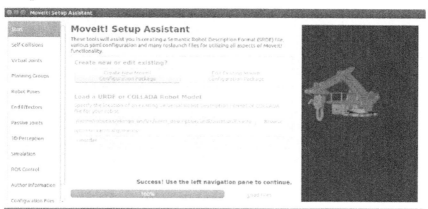

Figure 10.2: *Loading URDF file in MoveIt setup assistant*

Optimizing self-collision checking

This option generates a self-collision matrix, which finds the links on the robotic arm that are in collision and disables them. Collison is categorized into whether the links are always in collision, never in collision, with collision in the robot's default position, or whether the links are adjacent to each other on the kinematic chain. This process can help reduce the motion planning time. The number of random positions of the robot in which collision checking is done is decided based on the sampling density. The optimize self-collision checking window appears as shown in *figure 10.3*.

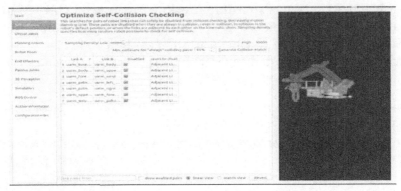

Figure 10.3: *Generating self-collision matrix for the robotic arm*

Defining planning groups

Planning groups are used to physically describe the robot, i.e., which parts of the robotic arm belong to the 'arm' and 'end effector' parts. For each link, its parent and child links are specified, describing the entire kinematics chain. The planning groups appear on the Moveit assistant window as shown in *figure 10.4*.

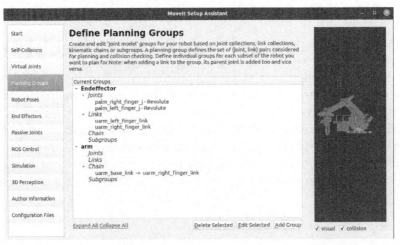

Figure 10.4: *Adding the planning groups*

To create a planning group, first click on the **Add group** button and then follow these steps:

1. Add the name of the planner (here, planner groups are named arm and end effector).

2. Choose the kinematics solver used for finding the inverse kinematics solution.

Defining robot pose

Some predefined poses can be set for the robotics arm, and these can be used as a reference position before performing path planning.

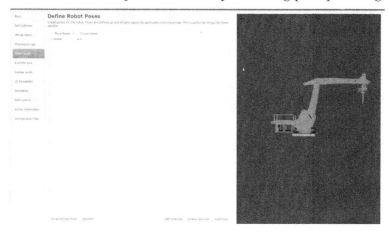

Figure 10.5: *Labeling the robot poses*

Click on the "**AddPose**" button and then move each joint of the robotic arm to the required position and select the corresponding planning group for the newly created robot pose.

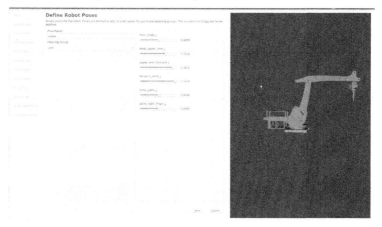

Figure 10.6: *Joint angle selection for the labeled robot pose*

Defining End effectors

The end effector in the robotic arm needs to be labeled as shown in *figure 10.7*. The group name and parent link name for the end effector needs to be given.

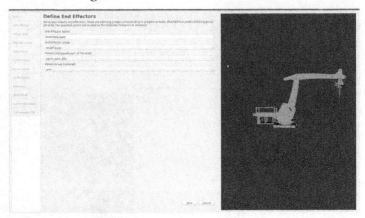

Figure 10.7: Defining the end effectors

Here, "**uarm_palm_link**" is the parent link for the end effector, and the end effector used is an external gripper that holds the end effector on its external surface.

Defining passive joints

Specify the joints in the robotic arm that are not actuated as passive joints. So, the joint states need not be published for these joints. In this robotic arm, every joint is actuated, so this can be left blank.

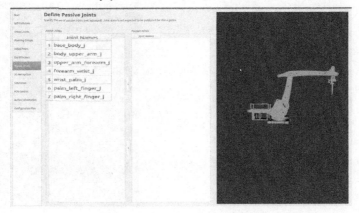

Figure 10.8: Adding passive joints

Setting up 3D perception sensors

The 3D perception option in MoveIt allows us to integrate 3D perception sensors like camera and **Light Detection and Ranging (LIDAR)** sensors to the robotic arm configuration. This is illustrated as follows:

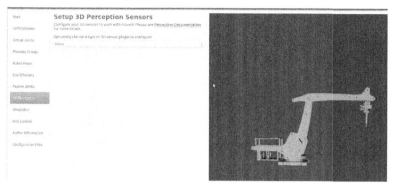

Figure 10.9: Adding 3D perception sensors

Simulating with gazebo

The simulation tool in MoveIt allows you to automatically generate the changes needed in the URDF file for the robot to carry out a task in the gazebo simulation environment.

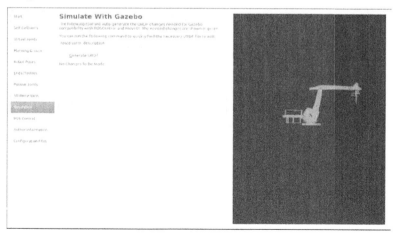

Figure 10.10: Configuring URDF for Gazebo simulation

Setting up ROS controllers

The ROS control tool is used to automatically generate the controllers for moving the robotic arm from one position to another by giving proper actuation commands and simultaneously tracking the joint states of the robot in a closed loop.

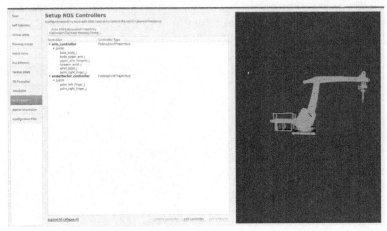

Figure 10.11: *Adding ROS controllers*

ROS control contains a set of packages that include controller interfaces, controller managers, transmission interfaces, and hardware interfaces. The joint state information read by the actuators input, along with a reference state information, is given as input to the ROS controller package. The ROS controller uses a closed loop feedback control mechanism like the **proportional integral derivative (PID)** controller to control the commands sent to the joint actuators.

Generating MoveIt configuration files

The '**Configuration Files**' option allows you to select the destination file location in which MoveIt configuration files for the robotic arm will be generated.

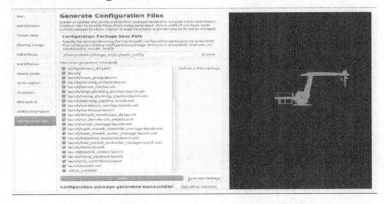

Figure 10.12: *Generating MoveIt configuration files*

After selecting the desired location, click on the **Generate package** button. This will create a motion planning package, which consists of a set of launch files and its related configuration files, for the robotic arm.

Planning and execution for the robotic arm

The MoveIt package **uarm_config** that was created for the robotic arm can be launched using the following command:

```
roslaunchuarm_configdemo.launch
```

The above command will launch the robotic arm with motion planning and execution capabilities in the RVIZ visualization window in ROS, as shown in *figure 10.13*:

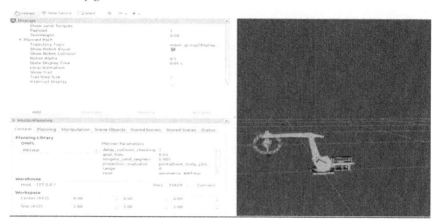

Figure 10.13: Planning and execution of the robotic arm in RVIZ

Different inverse kinematics solvers like RRTstar can be selected. The default inverse kinematic solver is RRTstar. In the planning tab, the starting robot state and goal robot state using the interactive markers seen in the RVIZ window at the **tool centre point** (**TCP**) of the robotic arm can be selected. In the planning tab, a 'Use Collision-Aware IK' checkbox can be seen. It gives an option to the inverse kinematics solver to plan a collision-free path. Before actual execution of the trajectory from the start state to the goal state, the 'plan' button can be clicked on to see how the robotic arm would switch states. After the planning is successful, this plan can be executed.

Conclusion

This chapter focused on how to create and use a motion planning package for a custom robotic arm. In this chapter, you learned how to use the MoveIt tool in ROS to find the forward and inverse kinematics solution while planning a path from source to goal location. This tool generates the ROS controllers needed for the movement of actuators in the robotic arm. Here, a Uarm robotic arm was used as an example to perform the motion planning tasks.

Sensors can be added in the robotic arm to get more intelligence and perform planning based on different behaviors. Here, the RVIZ GUI plugins and tools can be used to visualize the motion planning of the robotic arm. This package can be used directly with the physical robotic arm by making the necessary changes in the controller configurations.

In the next chapter, we will discuss the use and integration of computer vision into ROS.

Key terms

- **MoveIt elements**: MoveIt elements include the various functionalities from defining end effector to generating configuration files in MoveIt.

- **URDF model**: URDF file is a requirement for generating configuration files for custom robots.

CHAPTER 11
Vision

Introduction

In this chapter, you will learn how to integrate OpenCV with ROS. OpenCV is mainly used for image processing, machine vision, robotics operations, etc. OpenCV2 is the official supported version for ROS kinetic, but OpenCV3 can also be used. A package called "**vision_opencv**" is used to interface ROS with OpenCV. The "**vision_opencv**" package contains the following core packages:

- cv_bridge
- image_geometry

Structure

We will cover the following topics in this chapter:

- What is cv_bridge?
- Converting ROS image messages to OpenCV image formats
- Converting OpenCV image messages to ROS images messages

- ROS node example

- What is image geometry and camera calibration?

- Interfacing Astra 3D camera with ROS

- Interfacing Kinect camera with ROS

Objectives

After studying this chapter, various camera calibration procedures can be implemented using OpenCV in ROS. Additionally, you can convert a normal OpenCV program into a ROS OpenCV interface.

What is cv_bridge?

In ROS, the image data is of the sensor_msgs/Image type and in OpenCV, it is of the cv_Image type.

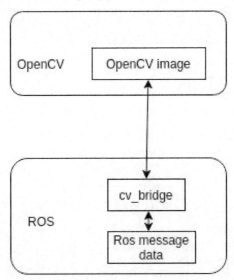

Figure 11.1: Conversion between OpenCV and ROS messages

Ros data format and OpenCV data format are different, so a library that handles the message data type conversion between them is needed; this is accomplished by **cv_bridge**. So, it acts as a bridge between ROS messages and OpenCV, as shown in *figure 11.1*. In this section, rospython is used to explain the data conversion from ROS Image messages to OpenCV Image messages and vice versa.

Converting ROS Image messages into OpenCV Image messages (rospython)

A `imgmsg_to_cv2` function from the `cv_bridge.CvBridge` module is used to convert ROS Image data into OpenCV image format:

```
cv_image = bridge.imgmsg_to_cv2(image_message, desired_
encoding="passthrough")
```

The above-mentioned function contains an OpenCV Image and its encoding. Here, "bridge" is an instance of the CvBridge class. The encoding refers to the destination CvImage. If the encoding is given a value passthrough, then the destination encoding will be the same as the source encoding. The following OpenCV image encodings can be used during the encoding process:

- 8UC[1-4]
- 8SC[1-4]
- 16UC[1-4]
- 16SC[1-4]
- 32SC[1-4]
- 32FC[1-4]
- 64FC[1-4]

Converting OpenCV image messages into ROS Image messages

The `cv2_to_imgmsg` function is used to convert an OpenCV image(cv:Mat) into ROS image message(sensor_msgs/Image).

```
image_message = bridge.cv2_to_imgmsg(cv_image,
encoding="passthrough")
```

The encoding refers to `cv:Mat`, but the `cv2_to_imgmsg` function does not perform any conversion. So, the destination ROS image will have the same number of channel and pixel intensity as the source `cv:Mat` image. However, the images in the format rgb8, bgr8 will insert special information in the image data. This will help you understand whether the received image is RGB or BGR.

ROS node example

The ROS node given below have the following dependencies:

- **sensor_msgs**
- **cv_bridge**
- **rospy**
- **std_msgs**

The ROS node is as follows:

```python
1.  #!/usr/bin/env python
2.  import roslib
3.  import sys
4.  import rospy
5.  import cv2
6.  from std_msgs.msg import String
7.  from sensor_msgs.msg import Image
8.  from cv_bridge import CvBridge, CvBridgeError
9.  class transform_image:
10.   def __init__(self):
11.       self.image_pub = rospy.Publisher("/cv2_to_
    rosimg",Image)
12.       self.bridge = CvBridge()
13.       self.image_sub = rospy.Subscriber("/usb_cam/
    image_raw",Image,self.callback)
14.       def callback(self,data):
15.         try:
16.             cv_image = self.bridge.imgmsg_to_
    cv2(data, "bgr8")
17.         except CvBridgeError as e:
18.             print(e)
19.         (rows,cols,channels) = cv_image.shape
20.         if cols > 60 and rows >60 :
```

```
21.                       cv2.circle(cv_image, (100,100), 8,
        (0,0,255),-1)
22.                       cv2.imshow("output window", cv_
        image)
23.                       cv2.waitKey(3)
24.                   try:
25.                       self.image_pub.publish(self.bridge.
        cv2_to_imgmsg(cv_image, "bgr8"))
26.               except CvBridgeError as e:
27.                   print(e)
28.           def main(args):
29.               im_tr = transform_image()
30.               rospy.init_node('image_converter',
        anonymous=True)
31.               try:
32.                   rospy.spin()
33.               except KeyboardInterrupt:
34.                   print("Shutting down")
35.                   cv2.destroyAllWindows()
36.           if __name__ == '__main__':
37.               main(sys.argv)
```

Here, the **usb_cam** ROS package is used get the live stream from the USB camera. It is launched using the following command:

roslaunchusb_camusb_cam-test.launch

It will publish the camera image stream on the **/usb_cam/image_raw** topic. The ROS node, subscribes to the **/usb_cam/image_raw** topic and converts it to OpenCV image using the **imgmsg_to_cv2(data, "bgr8")** function. The encoding method used here is **bgr8**. Then, a red circle is being drawn on the image using the **cv2.circle** OpenCV function. After the processing on the image, it is again converted into a ROS image using the **cv2_to_imgmsg(cv_image, "bgr8")** function. Then, it is published on to the ros topic **/cv2_to_rosimg**.

What is image_geometry?

The **image_geometry** package contains the cpp and python libraries for interpreting the geometric transformation in the image. It is usually used for interfacing the calibration parameters in the ROS messages of the "**sensor_msgs/CameraInfo**" type with the OpenCV functions such as the image rectification. While calibrating a camera in ROS, the calibration parameters will be saved in the "**sensor_msgs/CameraInfo**" message type.

Why camera calibration?

The camera hardware induces certain errors due to imperfections in the lens and image sensor. It is important to find the offset to deal with the following:

- Compensate for the lens distortion

- Find the dimensions of the object in frame

The camera parameters are composed of extrinsic and intrinsic parts. The 3D world image points and the corresponding 2D image points can then be used to detect the parameters needed to compensate the offset due to imperfections. To detect these parameters, a checkerboard of known dimensions is used to get the ground truth of 3D world image points, which can be compared to the image obtained from the camera. The calibration process is explained using the following block diagram:

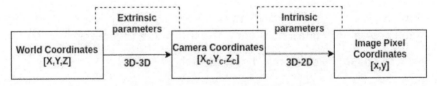

Figure 11.2: Camera calibration process

As illustrated in the block diagram in *figure 11.2*, the image points converted from the world coordinate system to camera coordinates considering the extrinsic parameters, resulting in a 3D-to-3D conversion. The next phase includes the conversion from camera coordinates to image pixel coordinates, resulting in a 3D-to-2D conversion.

Interfacing Astra 3D camera with ROS

In ROS, a package called **camera_calibration** is used, which uses the **opencv** camera calibration to calibrate the camera. Let's calibrate an Orbbec Astra camera. It is a powerful and reliable standalone 3D camera that consists of a normal RGB camera, an **Infrared** (IR) camera, and an IR projector. The depth information is obtained using the IR projector and the IR camera sensor.

Figure 11.3: *Orbbec Astra*

Package and driver installation

The drivers for Astra camera should be installed to access the device. Install the **astra_camera** ROS package to set up the drivers for Astra camera using the following command on a terminal:

```
sudo apt-get install ros-kinetic-astra-camera
```

A new **udev** rule needs to be created to detect the Astra camera. Udev rules use the device properties to identify a device irrespective of the port to which they are plugged in. The properties include device ID, vendor information, etc. Execute the following commands to start creating **udev** rules for the 3D camera:

```
cd  /etc/udev/rules.d/
```

Then, create a new file, as follows:

```
sudogedit 56-orbbec.rules
```

The following lines need to be added into the file:

```
SUBSYSTEM=="usb", ATTR{idProduct}=="0400",
ATTR{idVendor}=="2bc5", MODE:="0666", OWNER:="root",
GROUP:="video"

SUBSYSTEM=="usb", ATTR{idProduct}=="0401", ATTR{idVendor}=="2bc5",
```

```
MODE:="0666", OWNER:="root", GROUP:="video"

SUBSYSTEM=="usb", ATTR{idProduct}=="0402", ATTR{idVendor}=="2bc5",
MODE:="0666", OWNER:="root", GROUP:="video"

SUBSYSTEM=="usb", ATTR{idProduct}=="0403", ATTR{idVendor}=="2bc5",
MODE:="0666", OWNER:="root", GROUP:="video"

SUBSYSTEM=="usb", ATTR{idProduct}=="0404", ATTR{idVendor}=="2bc5",
MODE:="0666", OWNER:="root", GROUP:="video"

SUBSYSTEM=="usb", ATTR{idProduct}=="0405", ATTR{idVendor}=="2bc5",
MODE:="0666", OWNER:="root", GROUP:="video"

SUBSYSTEM=="usb", ATTR{idProduct}=="0406", ATTR{idVendor}=="2bc5",
MODE:="0666", OWNER:="root", GROUP:="video"

SUBSYSTEM=="usb", ATTR{idProduct}=="0407", ATTR{idVendor}=="2bc5",
MODE:="0666", OWNER:="root", GROUP:="video"

SUBSYSTEM=="usb", ATTR{idProduct}=="0408", ATTR{idVendor}=="2bc5",
MODE:="0666", OWNER:="root", GROUP:="video"

SUBSYSTEM=="usb", ATTR{idProduct}=="0409", ATTR{idVendor}=="2bc5",
MODE:="0666", OWNER:="root", GROUP:="video"

SUBSYSTEM=="usb", ATTR{idProduct}=="040a", ATTR{idVendor}=="2bc5",
MODE:="0666", OWNER:="root", GROUP:="video"
```

Now, the udev system needs to be restarted so that the recent changes reflect into the system:

```
sudo service udev reload
sudo service udev restart
```

The following command is used to test the Astra camera:

```
roslaunchastra_launchastra.launch
```

Intrinsic camera calibration

The focal point and optical center of a camera are the intrinsic parameters. On the other hand, the extrinsic parameters are the location and orientation of the camera and are independent of the camera properties. The program should be aware of these parameters to compensate for the errors. Astra 3D consists of two divisions, with **Red Green Blue (RGB)** and IR for 2D and depth images, respectively. Let's estimate the intrinsic parameters for the RGB and IR cameras.

Calibrating RGB camera

An 8×6 checkerboard is used to calibrate the camera. Checkerboards are normally used for multi-planar calibration because of their well-defined geometric structure and many natural interest points like corners and lines.

First, launch the Astra camera as given above and then run the camera calibration package as follows:

```
rosruncamera_calibration cameracalibrator.py image:=/
camera/rgb/image_raw camera:=/camera/rgb --size 8x6
--square 0.0245
```

Here, 0.0245 is the length of the square block in the checkerboard in meters. The RGB image data in the **/camera/rgb/image_raw** topic is obtained.

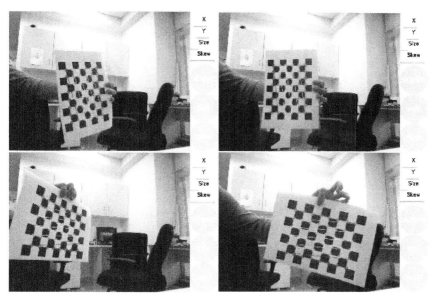

Figure 11.4: RGB camera calibration using checkerboards

Calibrating depth (IR) camera

For depth camera, the camera calibration package needs to be launched as follows:

```
rosruncamera_calibration cameracalibrator.py image:=/
camera/ir/image camera:=/camera/ir --size 8x6 --square
0.0245
```

Astra camera detects depth by using an IR camera and an IR speckle projector. During the calibration of the IR camera, it is impossible to detect checkerboard corners because of the IR speckle pattern. So, the IR projector needs to be covered with post-it notes or some transparent film to diffuse the IR speckle beams.

Figure 11.5: IR camera calibration using checkerboards

Camera calibration files

After getting adequate camera calibration data, the **COMMIT** and **SAVE** buttons on the GUI will get highlighted. Click on the **COMMIT** button, followed by the **SAVE** button. The camera calibration file will be saved in the **/.ros/camera_info** directory as a **.yaml** file. These calibrated parameters are then used during object pose and distance estimation. The calibration files will look like this:

```
image_width: 640
image_height: 480
camera_name: depth_Astra_Orbbec
camera_matrix:
  rows: 3
  cols: 3
    data:  [1225.085230184567,  0,  329.0617987028994,  0,
```

```
1361.481858948694, 126.7698415986929, 0, 0, 1]
distortion_model: plumb_bob
distortion_coefficients:
  rows: 1
  cols: 5
      data:   [0.08958639037954153,   12.31780630659108,
-0.151305333603155, 0.01633121092586805, 0]
rectification_matrix:
  rows: 3
  cols: 3
  data: [1, 0, 0, 0, 1, 0, 0, 0, 1]
projection_matrix:
  rows: 3
  cols: 4
   data: [1358.091552734375, 0, 330.5099333440266, 0, 0,
1469.306396484375, 112.6802256376013, 0, 0, 0, 1, 0]
```

Interfacing Kinect camera with ROS

The procedure to install the driver and calibration for Kinect is similar to the one mentioned in the previous section for an Astra 3D camera.

Package and driver installation

The drivers for Kinect can be installed using the following command:

```
sudo apt-get install ros-kinect-freenet-launch
```

Kinect does not necessarily need udev rules and can be launched and tested once the drivers are installed. Use the following command to launch the camera:

```
roslaunchfreenect_launchfreenect.launch
```

An alternative method to launch Kinect is by using **openni_launch** instead of **freenect_launch**.

Calibrating RGB camera

The procedure to calibrate Kinect is similar to the Astra 3D camera. Use the following command to calibrate an RGB camera for Kinect:

```
rosruncamera_calibration cameracalibrator.py image:=/
camera/rgb/image_raw camera:=/camera/rgb --size 8x6
--square 0.0245
```

Calibrating depth camera

Use the following command to calibrate depth camera for kinect:

```
rosruncamera_calibration cameracalibrator.py image:=/camera/
ir/image_raw camera:=/camera/ir --size 5x4 --square 0.0245
```

Interfacing Lidar with ROS

Lidar stands for Light Detection and Ranging. Lidar is a sensor that uses pulsed laser beams to measure spatial ranges. These ranges can then be stored and processed to represent meaningful spatial data. Lidars can be classified as 2D and 3D. An example of a 2D lidar is RPLidar. Similarly, Velodyne is an example of a 3D lidar. For now, we will consider the integration of 2D lidars into a ROS system, particularly the integration of RP Lidar with a system.

Installing Rplidar ROS Package

RPLidar has a **ros** package named **rplidarros**. This package has a driver that can convert the raw scanned data to **ros** Laser scan messages. Connect the device to the system using a USB port. If the current user has the required write permissions, the lidar can be directly launched using the following command:

```
roslaunchrplidar_rosview_rplidar.launch
```

If the current user account does not have the required permissions set, follow these steps:

1. Connect the device to the system.

2. Identify the device by scanning through the devices connected. Use the following command to list down the devices connected to the system:

   ```
   ls  -l /dev |grep ttyUSB
   ```

3. Provide write permissions for the USB port to which the lidar has been connected. Use the following command to give write permissions:

```
chmod 666 /dev/ttyUSB0
```

(Here, ttyUSB0 is the device identified using the preceding command.)

4. Once the permissions are given, the **roslaunch** command can be used to start the node and see the scanned result in RVIZ.

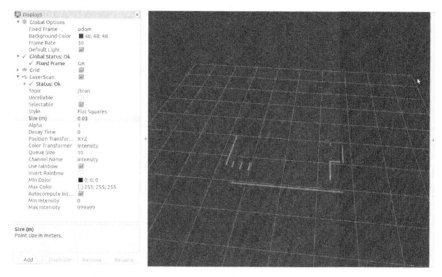

Figure 11.6: Laser scan data in RVIZ visualization tool

Conclusion

This chapter provided an introduction to using OpenCV in ROS with the help of an example. You learned how to integrate different sensors like Astra camera, Kinect camera, and Rplidar with ROS. The camera calibration procedures were also explained. This chapter explained how a normal OpenCV program can be converted into a ROS OpenCV interface by adding the necessary changes in the normal   programs.

In the next chapter, we will explore the use of Aruco markers for identification and tracking of the environment.

Key terms

- **ROS cv_bridge**: It is a library that provides an interface between OpenCV and ROS images.

- **Camera calibration**: It is the process of estimating the intrinsic and extrinsic parameters of a camera.

- **Kinect package and driver**: It refers to the required ROS Kinect packages and the corresponding drivers for interfacing the hardware.

- **ROS rplidar package**: It is a package developed to interface rplidar with a robot using ROS.

CHAPTER 12
Aruco Markers

Introduction

Aruco Markers are the signs or trackers used by imaging systems, and they can act as a reference point for measurements. Such markers are generally known as fiducial. Aruco is a binary square marker that can be used as a reference for measurements. These measurements can be used to track the camera position and orientation from the object. Each marker can also act as a unique identifier, assisting in object detection, environment tracking, and navigation.

Structure

We will cover the following topics in this chapter:

- Intrinsic parameters
- Marker dictionary and ID
- ROS package
- Camera calibration
- Implementation

- Implementing markers in gazebo
- Visualizing in gazebo

Objectives

In this chapter, you will understand the procedure of camera calibration and usage of Aruco markers.

Intrinsic parameters

There are specific requirements for tracking a marker, one of which is intrinsic parameters. Intrinsic parameters define the peculiarity, error, or properties of the sensors, which, in this case, is a 2D camera. The intrinsic parameters for a camera include properties like the optical center and focal length of the camera. These parameters help account for the distortion in the images and eventually, reduce errors. This process of estimating the intrinsic and extrinsic parameters of a camera is known as camera calibration.

Marker dictionary and ID

Aruco Markers are black and white and consist of a black border, which aids easy detection and tracking. The central part of the marker comprises a binary square that encodes the marker identifier. An identifier helps isolate the marker from a pool of corresponding markers in the dictionary. A dictionary can be defined as a collection of predefined markers, with each marker having a distinct identity. So, to start using an Aruco Marker, the dictionary should be specified. The program or the script would need two specific pieces of information to get started with identifying the markers:

Figure 12.1: Aruco Markers from dictionary - Aruco Original

- **Dictionary size**: The number of markers in a dictionary

- **Marker size**: The number of bits for each marker

The dictionary size is indirectly specified by selecting the dictionary name. The examples of Aruco dictionaries are 4*4, 5*5, aruco, and original. Once the dictionary name is specified in the code, the library fetches the respective number of markers and other relevant information. The marker size, which refers to the actual dimensions of the printed markers, is specified by the user. These dimensions help in the measurement of distance and marker tracking. The markers printed and used for the demonstration in this chapter are from the Aruco original dictionary.

ROS package

The packages required for you to get started with Aruco Marker detection are the usb cam package and the Aruco ROS package. Use the following command to install the above-mentioned packages:

```
Sudo apt-get install ros-kinetic-usb-cam ros-kinetic-
aruco-ros
```

The usb cam package helps publish the images captured from the usb camera as sensor messages. The images are converted into sensor messages to help other nodes process them and act accordingly. The Aruco ROS package is a ROS wrapper for libraries used in Aruco Marker detection.

Camera calibration

Camera calibration should be performed before implementing the packages on the system. Camera calibration helps reduce errors due to lens distortion and other intrinsic parameters. Here are the steps for calibration:

1. Install the **usb_cam** package:
   ```
   Sudo apt-get install ros-kinetic-usb-cam
   ```

2. Run the roscore:
   ```
   roscore
   ```

3. Open a new terminal and run the following:
   ```
   rosrunusb_camusb_cam_node
   ```

4. Open a new terminal and type this:

```
rosruncamera_calibration cameracalibrator.py --size
8x6 --square 0.02517 image:=/usb_cam/image_raw
camera:=/usb_cam
```

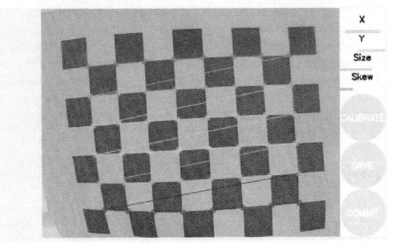

Figure 12.2: Camera calibration

5. Once the calibration window is active, move the checkered blocks page around to get multiple images. Once the required number of images are acquired, the calibrate button is activated and saved as a **.yaml** file. Once the commit button is pressed, it will save the **.yaml** file to the following:

/home/<username>/.ros/camera_info/head_camera.yaml

Implementation

There are two launch files required for the sample implementation of the Aruco detection. The first launch file publishes the images from usb camera, while the second launch file tracks the markers in the images obtained.

The publisher launch file is as follows:

```
1.  <launch>
2.  <arg name="video_device" default="/dev/video1" />
3.  <arg name="image_width" default="640" />
4.  <arg name="image_height" default="480" />
```

```
5.

6.   <node name="usb_cam" pkg="usb_cam" type="usb_cam_
     node" output="screen" >

7.   <param name="video_device" value="$(argvideo_
     device)" />

8.   <param name="image_width" value="$(argimage_width)"
     />

9.   <param name="image_height" value="$(argimage_
     height)"/>

10.  <param name="pixel_format" value="mjpeg" />

11.  <param name="camera_frame_id" value="usb_cam" />

12.  <param name="io_method" value="mmap"/>

13.  </node>

14.  </launch>
```

The launch file that leads to tracking of the marker is as follows:

```
1.   <launch>

2.   <arg name="markerId" default="12"/>

3.   <arg name="markerSize" default="0.025"/><!-- in
     meter -->

4.   <arg name="eye" default="left"/>

5.   <arg name="marker_frame" default="marker_frame"/>

6.   <arg name="ref_frame" default=""/><!-- Leave empty
     and the pose will be published wrt param parent_name
     -->

7.   <arg name="corner_refinement" default="LINES" />

8.   <node pkg="aruco_ros" type="single" name="aruco_
     single">

9.   <remap from="/camera_info" to="/usb_cam/camera_
     info" />

10.  <remap from="/image" to="/usb_cam/image_raw" />

11.  <param name="image_is_rectified" value="True"/>
```

```
12. <param name="marker_size"
    value="$(argmarkerSize)"/>

13. <param name="marker_id" value="$(argmarkerId)"/>

14. <param name="reference_frame" value="$(argref_
    frame)"/><!-- frame in which the marker pose will be
    referred -->

15. <param name="camera_frame" value="base_link"/>

16. <param name="marker_frame" value="$(argmarker_
    frame)" />

17. <param name="corner_refinement" value="$(argcorner_
    refinement)" />

18. </node>

19. </launch>
```

Save the above-mentioned launch files with their respective names into a package. To demonstrate the example, the package used here is **aruco_trial**. (Replace the package name with the respective packages while implementing.)

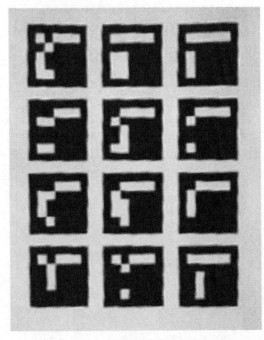

Figure 12.3: Image obtained from usb camera

Open a terminal and launch the publisher:

```
roslauncharuco_trialpublisher.launch
```

Open another terminal to launch the Aruco tracking node:

```
roslauncharuco_trialdetect.launch
```

Use rqt graph to view the markers being tracked and their respective axes.

Use the following command for using the rqt graph:

```
rosrunrqt_image_viewrqt_image_view
```

After the rqt window opens, select the relevant topics to view the results as shown in the following figure:

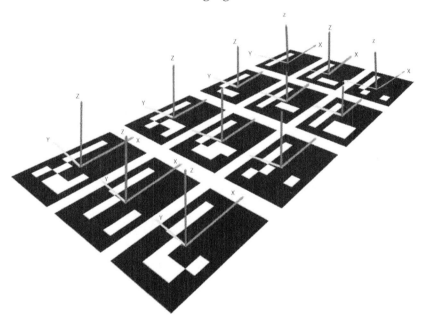

Figure 12.4: Tracked Aruco Markers

Implementing the marker in Gazebo

The Aruco Markers can be considered a part of the environment in which the robot is operational. So, let's place these markers in a virtual environment inside gazebo. The basic information and procedures regarding gazebo are covered in the gazebo chapter. As of now, let's further learn how to place the markers in gazebo.

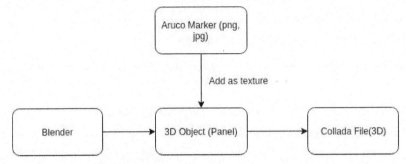

Figure 12.5: Block diagram for creating collada file

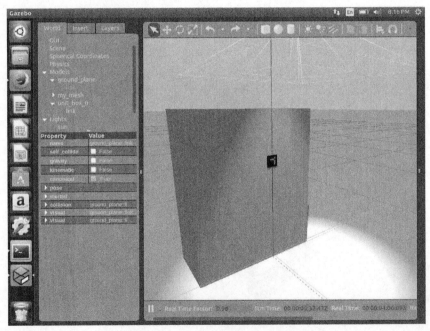

Figure 12.6: Aruco Marker inside Gazebo World

The output of the Collada file will be as shown in the preceding figure. The Aruco Marker panel is embedded in a wall in the gazebo world.

Blender

Blender is a computer graphics software that can be used for building 3D models. It is open source and can be downloaded from the official blender website. The Aruco image is put as a texture on the 3D model and then saved as a collada file. The following is the procedure to create the Aruco panel.

Open a new general file in blender. A cube will be present by default. The cube should be scaled down to the required size. In our application, the dimensions of the Aruco marker are as follows:

Length: 0.025 m

Width: 0.001 m

Height: 0.025 m

The dimensions can be adjusted from the transform panel. The parameters under the scale section should be changed to the above-mentioned dimensions, as shown here:

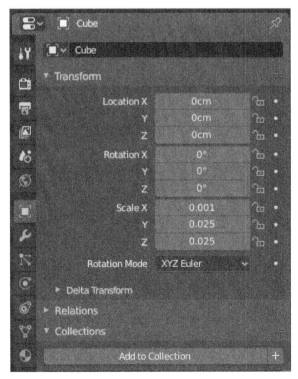

Figure 12.7: Transform section for adjusting the dimensions

The scale units are in meters, so ensure that you convert the marker dimensions to meters before entering it in the blender tab - Scale.

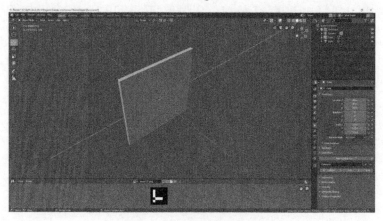

Figure 12.8: Panel for Aruco

Once the model is scaled to the required dimensions, the image texture needs to be added on the model. First, the image should be added to blender under the materials section.

Figure 12.9: Add image as base color

1. Add the image under the base color section. Do not assign the material yet.

2. The next step is to click on the object mode dropdown in the top-right corner. Select the edit mode.

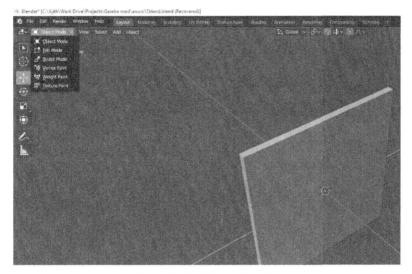

Figure 12.10: Edit mode option

3. The UV editing section opens once the edit mode is clicked on.

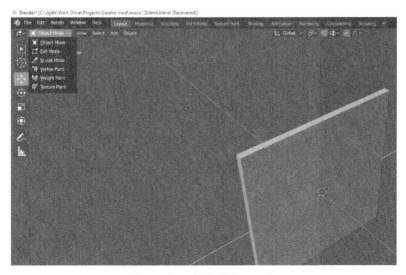

Figure 12.11: UV editing section

4. UV editing section opens a split window with provisions to add an image.

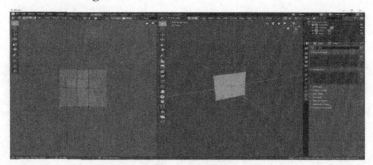

Figure 12.12: UV editing

5. The next step is to add the Aruco image:

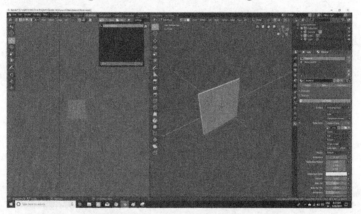

Figure 12.13: Add the Aruco image

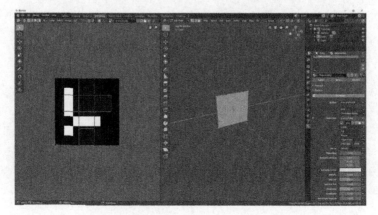

Figure 12.14: Aruco Image (To be scaled)

6. Add the Aruco image in the UV editing section, as illustrated in the preceding figure. The image added will not be in proportion to the object created.

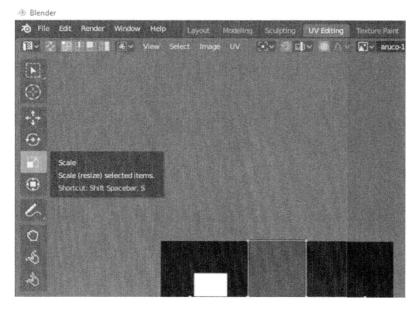

Figure 12.15: Option for scaling

The image should be scaled to fit on a single face of the 3D model created. The 3D model sections in the UV editing panel can be moved and scaled to adjust the image.

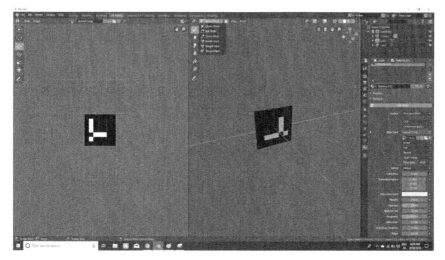

Figure 12.16: Texture mode (After scaling)

7. After scaling the sections according to the image, click on the edit mode dropdown option and click on **Texture** mode. Once the texture mode is clicked on, the rendering shows up on screen.

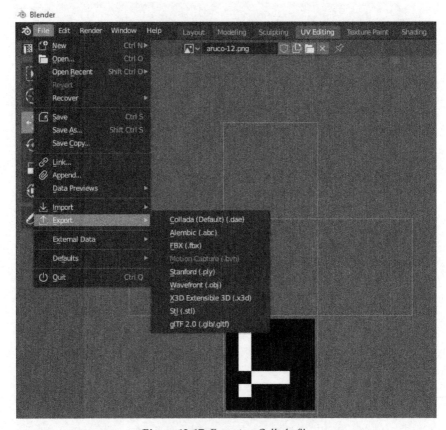

Figure 12.17: *Export as Collada file*

8. The final step is to export the 3D model as a Collada file. Click on `File | Export | Collada`, as shown in the preceding figure.

Visualizing in gazebo

The exported content from the blender includes the file with the `.dae` extension and the PNG image used as texture. Copy these files to a package or any specific folder. A world file is needed to launch the Aruco Marker into gazebo world. The following code can be used to create a simple world file:

```
1.    <?xml version="1.0"?>
2.    <sdf version="1.4">
3.    <world name="default">
4.    <include>
5.    <uri>model://ground_plane</uri>
6.    </include>
7.    <include>
8.    <uri>model://sun</uri>
9.    </include>
10.   <model name="my_mesh">
11.   <pose>0 0 0  0 0 0</pose>
12.   <static>true</static>
13.   <link name="body">
14.   <visual name="visual">
15.   <geometry>
16.   <mesh><uri>file://aruco12.dae</uri></mesh>
17.   </geometry>
18.   </visual>
19.   </link>
20.   </model>
21.   </world>
22.         </sdf>
```

Save the file in the same folder as the **.dae** file with the **.world** extension. Ensure that you change the name of the Collada file in the following line. The Collada file used here is **aruco12.dae**:

```
<mesh><uri>file://aruco12.dae</uri></mesh>
```

grey

aruco12.dae

aruco-12.png

gazebo_model_
test.world

Figure 12.18: Collada and world file

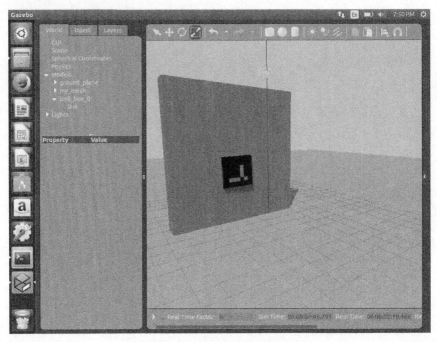

Figure 12.19: Aruco Marker in Gazebo World

Now, open a terminal in the above-mentioned folder and open the world file in gazebo using the following command (the name of the world file is **gazebo_model_test.world**):

```
gazebo gazebo_model_test.world
```

This will open the Aruco Marker in gazebo world. Other components can also be added to the environment, like simple shapes, models from databases, and other structures; save the new world along with the Aruco Marker. The marker can also be rotated and displaced around the gazebo world. The world can be saved by going to **File | Save World as** - (enter the name).

Conclusion

In this chapter, you learned how Aruco Markers function and understood the significance of marker dictionaries. We also explored the use, generation, and detection of Aruco markers using ROS packages. Additionally, we discussed the process to build and import a 3D model of an Aruco marker.

In the next chapter, we will take a look at the navigation of autonomous robots using simultaneous localization and mapping.

Key terms

- **Marker dictionary and ID**: It refers to a collection of aruco markers with specific ID. It would be impossible to detect the markers without knowing the dictionary.

- **aruco ROS package**: This package provides the necessary nodes and configuration files for Aruco marker-based implementations in ROS.

- **gazebo world**: It refers to all objects and settings in a simulated environment except the robot.

CHAPTER 13
Slam

Introduction

Mobility is a great feat of evolution. Many animal and bird species have developed highly advanced orientating and homing abilities. Compared to such species, the navigational capabilities of human beings are less advanced. However, an average human being can still navigate through familiar and unfamiliar landscapes using multiple sensory inputs such as visual, auditory, and even olfactory. In human beings, the hippocampus and prefrontal cortex of the brain play pivotal roles in planning and navigating simultaneously, to give a sense of location, direction, and distance. This interlinking and complex function that involves billions of neurons and millions of connections are to be simulated to navigate a robot.

The process of navigation shall be split into three steps:

- Spatial coding
- Landmark anchoring
- Route planning

To control the movements of a robot effectively around an environment, it is essential to locate the robot relative to its environment, its directions of movement, and the distances traveled. The breaking down of this process begins with spatial coding and landmark anchoring, which sums up to mapping of the environment. This is a hard problem. The location and map parameters are uncertain and relative to each other; this requires a solution of looped concepts of localization, which is relative to the map and that of mapping, which, in turn, is relative to the position estimate (location) of the object. Any error in data associations can lead to disastrous consequences or divergence. This seemingly chicken-or-egg dilemma required a solution that can resolve both issues simultaneously.

SLAM was developed to meet this need.

Structure

We will cover the following topics in this chapter:

- What is SLAM ?
- Different approaches to SLAM
- Autonomous navigation
- Move base package

Objectives

After studying this chapter, you will be able to navigate a robotic system and explore the relevant ROS packages for mapping, hardware integration, and calibration.

What is SLAM?

Simultaneous Localization And Mapping (SLAM) is an approach developed in the mid-1980s. This method can be used to learn a map and locate the robot simultaneously. Solving SLAM is an essential requirement for any robotic movement to be fully automated. There are multiple methods used to implement SLAM algorithms; most are based on probabilistic concepts.

Different approaches to SLAM

There are several approaches to perform SLAM. Some of the most popular approaches include the following:

- Gmapping

- Hector Slam

- Kartographer SLAM

- OpenSLAM

OpenSLAM is one of the most popular open-source libraries available for implementing SLAM algorithms in an application. However, it will not be used for the task at hand. The ROS community offers several wrappers, which are standalone algorithms or libraries, that enable the implementation of SLAM via ROS. Let's consider one of the most popularly used wrappers known as Gmapping.

Gmapping requires two sets of data to function: an odometry source, either from the rotation of wheels or motion sensors, and the laser data to create the environment around the robot.

Gmapping is mostly used in large environments where just the laser input is not sufficient to localize the robot, i.e., in areas with boundaries that are much further than the range of the laser scanner. In such cases, the distance traveled by the wheels is also used to localize the robot.

Performing SLAM

The various steps involved in performing SLAM are detailed in the following sections.

Preparing the URDF

TheURDF file should be modified to use it for the simulation. Following are the steps to add plugins to the URDF file.

1. o perform SLAM, a TF tree is needed, as shown here:

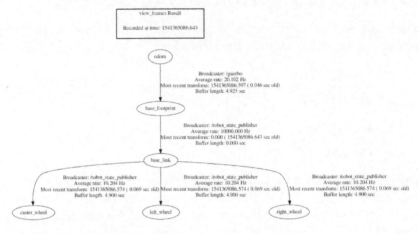

Figure 13.1: Tf Tree for basic differential drive robot

2. In the URDF created in *Chapter 7, Designing a Robot*, add a laser link and joint, as follows:

```
1.  <link name="laser_link">
2.  <visual>
3.  <origin xyz="0 0 0" rpy="0 0 0" />
4.  <geometry>
5.  <cylinder length="0.02" radius="0.05"/>
6.  </geometry>
7.  <material name="Blue" />
8.  </visual>
9.  </link>
10. <joint name="base_laser_joint" type="fixed">
11. <origin xyz="0 0 0.08" rpy="0 0 0" />
12. <parent link="base_footprint"/>
13. <child link="laser_link" />
14. </joint>
15. <gazebo reference="laser_link">
16. <material>Gazebo/Blue</material>
```

```
17.  <turnGravityOff>false</turnGravityOff>
18.  <sensor type="ray" name="laser_sensor">
19.  <pose>0 0 0 0 0 0</pose>
20.  <visualize>true</visualize>
21.  <update_rate>100</update_rate>
22.  <ray>
23.  <scan>
24.  <horizontal>
25.  <samples>720</samples>
26.  <resolution>1</resolution>
27.  <min_angle>-1.570796</min_angle>
28.  <max_angle>4.71239</max_angle>
29.  </horizontal>
30.  </scan>
31.  <range>
32.  <min>0.10</min>
33.  <max>100.0</max>
34.  <resolution>0.001</resolution>
35.  </range>
36.  </ray>
37.  <plugin name="gazebo_ros_head_hokuyo_
     controller" filename="libgazebo_ros_laser.so">
38.  <topicName>/scan</topicName>
39.  <frameName>laser_link</frameName>
40.  </plugin>
41.  </sensor>
42.  </gazebo>
```

3. To run the robot as a differential drive robot in gazebo, a
    plugin must be added that converts **cmd_vel** topics to wheel
    velocities:

```
1.  <gazebo>
2.  <plugin name="differential_drive_controller"
    filename="libgazebo_ros_diff_drive.so">
```

```
3.  <legacyMode>false</legacyMode>

4.  <rosDebugLevel>Debug</rosDebugLevel>

5.  <publishWheelTF>false</publishWheelTF>

6.  <robotNamespace>/</robotNamespace>

7.  <publishTf>1</publishTf>

8.  <publishWheelJointState>false</
    publishWheelJointState>

9.  <alwaysOn>true</alwaysOn>

10. <updateRate>100.0</updateRate>

11. <leftJoint>front_right_wheel_joint</leftJoint>

12. <rightJoint>front_left_wheel_joint</rightJoint>

13. <wheelSeparation>${2*base_radius}</
    wheelSeparation>

14. <wheelDiameter>${2*wheel_radius}</
    wheelDiameter>

15. <broadcastTF>1</broadcastTF>

16. <wheelTorque>30</wheelTorque>

17. <wheelAcceleration>1.8</wheelAcceleration>

18. <commandTopic>cmd_vel</commandTopic>

19. <odometryFrame>odom</odometryFrame>

20. <odometryTopic>odom</odometryTopic>

21. <robotBaseFrame>base_footprint</robotBaseFrame>

22. </plugin>

23. </gazebo>
```

While running SLAM in gazebo (in a simulation), the differential drive plugin mentioned in the URDF will provide the odometry values to localize the robot. On the other hand, for a physical robot, the encoder values must be noted and converted into **rotations per minute (RPM)**. Then, use inverse kinematics to calculate the velocity of the robot in x, y, and z directions. This data should then be published in the /odom topic. By launching RVIZ, the following robot can be viewed:

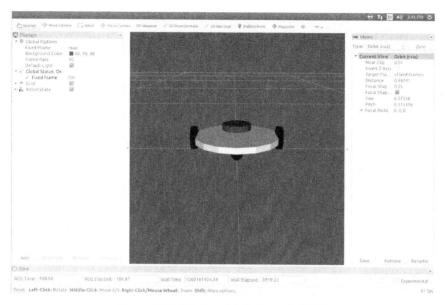

Figure 13.2: *Robot model displayed in RVIZ*

Setting up the packages for Gmapping

ROS has packages for Gmapping, which is an efficient particle filter for learning grid maps. The following steps are involved in the procedure to set up the ROS Gmapping packages:

1. To generate a map, the SLAM library is required. Let's install a Gmapping library from ROS repositories. Run the following command to do so:

```
sudo apt-get install ros-kinetic-gmapping
```

2. Once the libraries are installed, the node can be called by modifying the launch files:

```
1.  <launch>
2.  <!-- these are the arguments you can pass this
    launch file, for example paused:=true -->
3.  <arg name="paused" default="false"/>
4.  <arg name="use_sim_time" default="true"/>
5.  <arg name="gui" default="true"/>
6.  <arg name="headless" default="false"/>
```

7. `<arg name="debug" default="false"/>`

8. *`<!-- We resume the logic in empty_world.launch, changing only the name of the world to be launched -->`*

9. `<include file="$(find gazebo_ros)/launch/empty_world.launch">`

10. `<arg name="world_name" value="$(find my_robot)/worlds/world.world"/>`

11. *`<!-- more default parameters can be changed here -->`*

12. `</include>`

13. *`<!-- Load the URDF into the ROS Parameter Server -->`*

14. `<param name="robot_description" command="$(find xacro)/xacro.py $(find my_robot)/urdf/differential_wheeled_robot.xacro" />`

15. `<node name="joint_state_publisher" pkg="joint_state_publisher" type="joint_state_publisher"></node>`

16. *`<!-- start robot state publisher -->`*

17. `<node pkg="robot_state_publisher" type="state_publisher" name="robot_state_publisher" output="screen" >`

18. `<param name="publish_frequency" type="double" value="50.0" />`

19. `</node>`

20. `<node pkg="gmapping" type="slam_gmapping" name="gmapping"></node>`

21. `<node pkg="rviz" type="rviz" name="rviz"></node>`

22. `</launch>`

3. Bring up the robot in gazebo by running the following command:

```
rosrunmy_robotmy_robot.launch
```

4. Now, an empty world in gazebo with the robot loaded inside it can be viewed. Obstacles can be generated around the robot by clicking on the different 'objects' buttons on the toolbar. The current world can be   edited, and walls and other boundaries can be added by going to the edit world section of gazebo. To reuse this world, save it in a 'worlds' directory in the **my_robot/ directory**. Now, modify the launch file as follows:

```
1.   <arg name="world_name" value="$(find my_robot)/
     worlds/myworld.world"/>
```

Once the robot is loaded in the world, it can be moved using teleop. Run the following command in another terminal to do so:

rosrunteleop_twist_keyboard teleop_twist.py

If teleop is not installed, it can be installed by running the following command:

sudo apt-get install ros-<your distro>-teleop-twist-*

Once the robot starts navigating the Gazebo world, the map will be created as shown in *figure 13.3*.

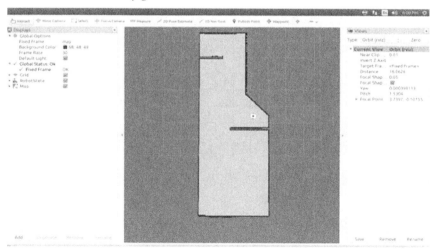

Figure 13.3: *Map created in RVIZ*

5. Using the RVIZ display pane, add the topics to be visualized. Here, the scan, robotstate, and map topics to be displayed are

needed. Once these are selected, the robot can be viewed by creating a map as follows:

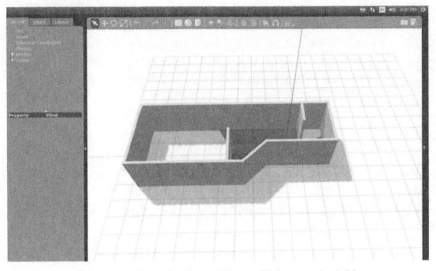

Figure 13.4: Robot inside a gazebo world, laser ray is visible

6. By using teleop, the robot can be navigated around the gazebo world and can see that the map is updated as it moves along. Once satisfied with the generated map, it should be saved. To do this, open a terminal, navigate to the **maps** folder in the **my_robot** directory, and run the following command:

```
rosrunmap_servermap_savermap_test.pgm
```

Autonomous navigation

To perform autonomous navigation, the following activities must be initiated:

- Obtain a map of the environment and publish this data

- Localize the robot on the map

- Obtain a path to travel from source to destination

- Provide velocity commands to the base to travel from source to destination

- Continuously update this path when an obstacle is encountered

The navigation stack in ROS helps us fulfill these activities.

The navigation stack

The ROS Navigation stack is a set of packages that enables us to perform the autonomous navigation of a robot in an unknown environment. The job of the stack is to take information from distance sensors, odometry sensors, and goal positions and provide velocity parameters to the wheels of the robot.

A simple block diagram for the navigation stack is as follows:

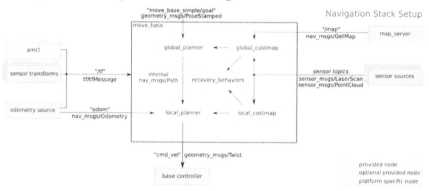

Figure 13.5: Navigation stack

The steps involved in autonomous navigation are described in the following sections.

Obtaining a map of the environment

To obtain a map of the environment, a mapping algorithm similar to SLAM performed in the previous section of this chapter must be performed. This map can then be saved and published in the /map topic using the map server package. The map obtained during SLAM is stored as a **.yaml** file. Run the following command to enable the map server to publish the map data:

```
rosrunmap_servermap_servermap_test.pgml
```

Output Topic: Map (/map)

Localizing the robot in the map

An algorithm for localizing the robot in the 2D environment is required. AMCL is a commonly used algorithm, and it uses the robots odometry, laser data, and map data to localize the robot in the environment.

AMCL3

Adaptive Monte-Carlo Localization (AMCL) is a probabilistic algorithm to approximate the position of the robot in an unknown 2D environment. The package takes in data from various sensors to approximate the position of the robot.

The inputs required for AMCL are as follows:

- Laser data (/scan)
- Odometry (/odom)
- Approximate Starting position of the robot (/currentPose)
- Map of the environment(/map)

These data sets are combined, and a probable transform of the robot for the map is published as output. This package aims to provide a transformation between the odometry information of the robot and the map of the environment.

For AMCL to work properly, there should be a connection between odometry and the laser scan topics. Ensure that the TF Tree has the connection before moving on to the next step.

Obtain a path to travel from source to destination

To travel from source to destination, the shortest path between the two points needs to be calculated. This can be implemented using multiple algorithms, like Dijkstra's Algorithm or A* algorithm. A package called **move_base** is used in navigation stack, which performs the various functions listed above.

Move base package

The move base package consists of nodes that accept the transform from AMCL, map data and sensor data, and the goal and calculates the velocity commands required for moving the robot from source to destination. The two important components of **move_base** are the global planner and the local planner.

The global planner

The aim of the global planner is to provide the shortest path between the current position of the robot and the goal destination. The global planner only considers the radius of the robot and map data to generate this path. It provides the most direct path that the robot should try to follow to reach the destination. The map of the environment is converted to the global costmap to achieve this.

The global costmap

The global costmap is simply a version of the map of the environment with the walls and obstacles in the map being provided as an inflation radius. The region around the walls is denoted in the environment to prevent the robot from getting too close to the walls of the environment.

The local planner

The local planner aims to provide velocities to the mobile base by looking at the path created and the local costmap. The local planner updates the path provided by the global planner to accommodate dynamic and moving obstacles and alters the path accordingly.

The local costmap

The local costmap is a grid created around the vicinity of the robot using laser data and considering the inflation radius. The local costmap data is updated when the robot moves.

Recovery_behaviors

These behaviors are executed in case the robot loses track of its environment or gets stuck between obstacles. The robot attempts to clear out dynamic obstacles and tries to generate a new local path. It may also perform a full rotation to do so. If the robot can recover its position, the local planner again generates a path. Otherwise, it sends a signal that it has failed and manual intervention is necessary. This can be enabled or disabled as per requirement.

Navigating the robot in gazebo

The next stage includes navigating the robot in the virtual world created in gazebo. Following are the steps to start the navigation.

1) To navigate the mobile robot in gazebo, the navigation stack must be installed inside the workspace.

```
sudo apt-get install ros-kinetic-navigation-stack
```

2) Once this is completed, ensure that **move_base** and AMCL are installed. To begin with, it is necessary to perform the localization of the robot. In the launch file prepared in the previous section of this chapter, remove the line that calls the Gmapping node. Now, add the AMCL package and call it in the launch file.

3) Run the launch file:

```
roslaunchmy_robotamcl.launch
```

The robot can be seen in RVIZ, as shown here:

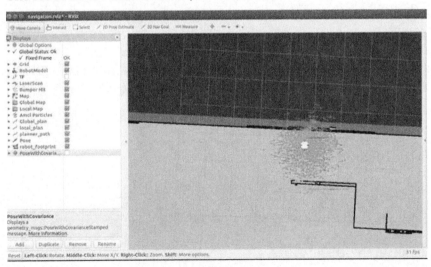

Figure 13.6: Initial pose of the robot

4) Using the **2D Pose Estimate** button, an approximate position of the robot can be specified in the 2D space. This will cause AMCL to approximate the position of the robot in that point of space. To move the robot around the workspace, launch teleop twist keyboard by running the following command:

```
rosrunteleop_twist_keyboard teleop_twist_keyboard.py
```

5) Navigate the robot around the gazebo world and check whether it is moving around in RVIZ.

6) Once AMCL is set up, the robot can be moved by using **move_base**. **Move_base** has several parameters that need to be set up. Edit the launch file to include **move_base.xml**.

   ```
   <include file="$(find my_robot)/launch/includes/move_base.launch.xml"/>
   ```

The **<move_base.launch>** file is as follows:

```
1.  <launch>

2.  <arg name="odom_topic" default="odom" />

3.  <node pkg="move_base" type="move_base"
    respawn="false" name="move_base" output="screen">

4.  <rosparam file="$(find my_robot)/param/costmap_
    common_params.yaml" command="load" ns="global_
    costmap" />

5.  <rosparam file="$(find my_robot)/param/costmap_
    common_params.yaml" command="load" ns="local_
    costmap" />

6.  <rosparam file="$(find my_robot)/param/local_costmap_
    params.yaml" command="load" />

7.  <rosparam file="$(find my_robot)/param/global_
    costmap_params.yaml" command="load" />

8.  <rosparam file="$(find my_robot)/param/base_local_
    planner_params.yaml" command="load" />

9.  <rosparam file="$(find my_robot)/param/dwa_local_
    planner_params.yaml" command="load" />

10. <rosparam file="$(find my_robot)/param/move_base_
    params.yaml" command="load" />

11. </node>

12. </launch>
```

7) This launch file sets various parameters for the local and global planners. The **launch/includes/** folder contains the parameters that are set. Now, to navigate the robot around

the environment, set a pose for the robot initially. Click on the 2D Nav Goal button to give it a goal.

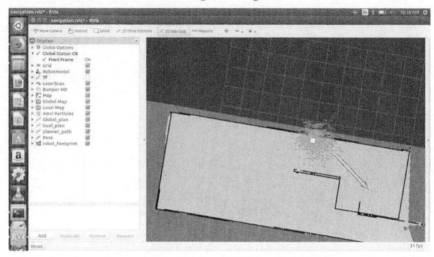

Figure 13.7: Providing the destination pose to the robot

The robot will reach its destination after the navigation is complete.

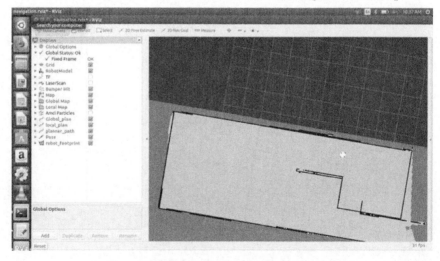

Figure 13.8: Robot after reaching the destination

Conclusion

In this chapter, we provided an overview of the navigation of a robotic system. We also covered some important technical elements that play a role in the successful implementation of SLAM, along with different packages that can be used in mapping, hardware integration, and calibration.

In the next chapter, we will look at the usage of commands and sensor data from a mobile device. The data from the mobile device will be fetchedusing react native apps. These data will be eventually used to control a ROS based robot..

Key terms

- **Approaches to SLAM**: Simultaneous localization and mapping can be implemented using multiple methods and approaches.

- **Gmapping**: It is a Rao-Blackwellized particle filter-based algorithm for implementing SLAM.

- **Navigation stack**: It is a collection of packages that takes information from sensors and has command velocities as output, helping a robot reach its goal position.

- **Gazebo plugins**: It is a script that can be compiled as a shared library and inserted into the simulation. It has access to all the functionalities in gazebo.

CHAPTER 14
React Native App

Introduction

Mobile apps have made life easier in various ways. Now, they have the power to link many devices and exchange information. An app is a hub that can leverage sensors and communication to do amazing things with technology. It is already happening, and this relationship will grow as more devices are created and more apps are developed.

Structure

We will cover the following topics in this chapter:

- Opportunities
- Mobile application development framework
- React native
- App development
- Capturing accelerometer, gyroscope, and magnetometer value

- Establishing a connection between ROS server and react native app
- Connection with Non-ROS programs
- ROS bridge suite

Objectives

After studying this chapter, you will be able to create a robust mobile application to manage a robotic system.

Opportunities

Mobile devices are already empowered with apps and sensors that can reveal detailed information about their users. In addition to geo-location information, smartphones and tablets can trace light conditions, the orientation of the device, and a lot more.

Mobile devices are equipped with communication modules like Wifi, Bluetooth, and NFC, along with sensors that can track the surrounding environment. These capabilities enable them to communicate with other similar smart systems. IoT will also enable remote operation of the office access system and even monitoring one's garage door from anywhere. Mobile connectivity and in-built sensors strengthen the IoT ecosystem, creating a new world of opportunities and development in education, travel, healthcare, retail, and many other industries.

IoT will have a big impact on our environment and economy in the future. The significance of smartphones will further increase in the near future when these mobile devices will be used as a primary interface to connect to virtually anything and everything. All the innovation and developments in IoT world will make our lives better.

Let's get familiar with mobile application development.

Mobile application development framework

A mobile development framework is a software framework designed to support mobile app development.

Types of mobile development frameworks

Just like there are many web frameworks for building websites and web applications, there are quite a few frameworks out there for mobile development.

The mobile development frameworks covered in the following sections fall under the following types:

- Native mobile development frameworks

- Cross-platform development frameworks

Native mobile app development

Most of the mobile frameworks out there are for cross-platform development. Generally, native mobile app development is done using frameworks created and maintained by the company that owns the mobile platform, so there is usually just one of those.

In the case of iOS, the iOS **Software Development Kit (SDK)** is customarily used with XCode, which is an IDE. For native Android app development, the Android SDK is used with Android Studio as the IDE of choice. The frameworks are contained in the SDKs, and each one has the programming languages used with them. Swift or Objective-C for iOS, and Kotlin or Java for Android.

Native apps are generally known to be fast. They are compatible with the device's hardware and native features like the camera, accelerometer, etc. On the other hand, they can be quite expensive. A mobile app in the IoT domain must target all the major mobile platforms, mainly Android and iOS.

This means that they would require separate development teams to develop an app for their business. They would also have to maintain the app after deployment; one can only imagine how expensive a setup that can be.

Cross-platform mobile app development

Cross-platform mobile frameworks are created to develop mobile apps for more than just one platform. Most, if not all the popular cross-platform frameworks out there, support development for majorly Android and iOS.

The following are the cross-platform mobile app development frameworks widely used by developers:

- Ionic

- Xamarin

- React Native

- Flutter

Each cross-platform mobile app development framework has its own pros and cons. In this chapter, you will focus on the React Native framework and understand how the best mobile apps for IoT can be developed.

React Native

React Native is a JavaScript framework for writing real, natively rendering mobile applications for iOS and Android. It's based on React, Facebook's JavaScript library for building user interfaces, but instead of targeting the browser, it targets mobile platforms. In other words, web developers can now write mobile applications that look and feel truly native, all from the comfort of a JavaScript library that is already known. Plus, most of the code written can be shared between platforms, so React Native makes it easy to simultaneously develop for both Android and iOS platforms, which are widely used by the end users.

Just like React for the Web, React Native applications are written using a mixture of JavaScript and XML-esque mark-up, known as JSX. Then, under the hood, the React Native bridge invokes the native rendering APIs in Objective-C (for iOS) or Java (for Android). Thus, the application will be rendered using real mobile UI components, not WebView, and they will look and feel like any other mobile application. React Native also exposes JavaScript interfaces for platform APIs, so React Native apps can access platform features like the phone camera, user's location, or the other sensors.

React Native currently supports both iOS and Android, and it has the potential to expand to future platforms as well. In this book, we will discuss both iOS and Android. A vast majority of the code written will be cross-platform, and yes, React Native can be used to build production-ready mobile applications. Some anecdotes: Facebook,

TaskRabbit, Instagram, Uber Eats, Discord, and Airbnb are already using it in production for user-facing applications.

App development

The React Native team has baked strong developer tools and meaningful error messages into the framework, so working with robust tools is a part of the development experience.

For instance, because React Native is just JavaScript, the application need not be rebuilt to see the reflected changes; instead, you can use CMD+R or CTRL+M to refresh the application, just like for any other web page. All those minutes spent waiting for the application to build can really add up, and in contrast, React Native's quick iteration cycle feels like a godsend.

Additionally, React Native lets developers take advantage of intelligent debugging tools and error reporting. The developer tools from Chrome or Safari can also be used for mobile development. Likewise, any text editor of the developer's preference can be used; React Native does not force you to work in XCode to develop for iOS or Android Studio for Android development.

The following are the pre-requisites:

Operating System:

Windows (or) Linux (or) Mac OS

Software's:

Java(1.8.0 or above)

Node JS (10.0.0 or above)

NPM (6.0.0 or above)

Yarn (1.17.0 or above)

React-Native-Cli (2.0.0 or above)

Visit the link given here and follow the instructions for pre-requisites installation guidelines:

https://facebook.github.io/react-native/docs/getting-started

Here are the commands to remember:

```
react-native init<Project-Name>
```

Keep in mind that the app name must be camelCase! No kebab-case!
:)

cd (Change Directory) into the respective folder directory and to run
the application, type the following:

IOS: `$ react-native run-ios`

Android: `$ react-native run-android`

Instructions for generating a signed APKto publish in the Android
Play Store and generating build for IOS App Store submission are
available in the following links:

Android: **https://facebook.github.io/react-native/docs/signed-apk-android**

IOS: **https://facebook.github.io/react-native/docs/0.60/running-on-device#building-your-app-for-production**

Additionally, ensure that the following environmental variables are
configured in the machine:

```
export ANDROID_HOME=$HOME/Library/Android/sdk
```

```
export PATH=$PATH:$ANDROID_HOME/emulator
```

```
export PATH=$PATH:$ANDROID_HOME/tools
```

```
export PATH=$PATH:$ANDROID_HOME/tools/bin
```

```
export PATH=$PATH:$ANDROID_HOME/platform-tools
```

```
export emulator='$ANDROID_HOME/tools/emulator'
```

```
export JAVA_HOME=/Library/Java/JavaVirtualMachines/
adoptopenjdk-8.jdk/Contents/Home/
```

Capturing accelerometer, gyroscope, and magnetometer values

The package used in this example is "react-native-sensors". More
details about the usage of this package are available at **https://github.
com/react-native-sensors/react-native-sensors**.

The following is the sample code to capture the accelerometer values from the device to either display or send them to the robot as per application:

AccelerometerScreen.js

```javascript
import React, { Component } from 'react';
import {
  StyleSheet,
  Text,
  View
} from 'react-native';

import { accelerometer, setUpdateIntervalForType,
SensorTypes } from "react-native-sensors";

const Value = ({name, value}) => (
  <View style={styles.valueContainer}>
    <Text style={styles.valueName}>{name}:</Text>
    <Text style={styles.valueValue}>{new String(value).
substr(0, 8)}</Text>
  </View>
)

export default class AccelerometerScreen extends
Component {
  constructor(props) {
    super(props);
    this.state = {
        x: 0,
        y: 0,
        z: 0,
        timestamp: 0,
    };
  }

  componentDidMount(){
    setUpdateIntervalForType(SensorTypes.accelerometer, 500);
    const subscription = accelerometer.subscribe(({ x, y,
z, timestamp }) =>
```

```
        this.setState({ x, y, z, timestamp })
    // This line will set the x, y, z, timestamp values
to the state also we can send these values to the ros
server via web socket protocol.
    );
  }

  render() {
    return (
      <View style={styles. Container}>
        <Text style={styles.headline}>
          Accelerometer values
        </Text>
        <Value name="x" value={this.state.x} />
        <Value name="y" value={this.state.y} />
        <Value name="z" value={this.state.z} />
      </View>
    );
  }
}

const styles = Stylesheet. Create({
  container: {
    flex: 1,
    justifyContent: 'center',
    alignItems: 'center',
    backgroundColor: '#F5FCFF',
  },
  headline: {
    fontSize: 30,
    textAlign: 'center',
    margin: 10,
  },
  valueContainer: {
    flexDirection: 'row',
    flexWrap: 'wrap',
  },
```

```
    valueValue: {
      width: 200,
      fontSize: 20
    },
    valueName: {
      width: 50,
      fontSize: 20,
      fontWeight: 'bold'
    },
    instructions: {
      textAlign: 'center',
      color: '#333333',
      marginBottom: 5,
    },
});
```

The preceding code captures the accelerometer value from the device and displays it as shown in *figure 14.1*:

Figure 14.1: Screenshot of accelerometer values

The **gyroscopescreen.js** code captures the gyroscope values from the device and displays them on the screen. The code can be further modified to transmit the sensor values over a wireless network as per the application:

GyroscopeScreen.js

```js
import React, { Component } from 'react';
import {
  StyleSheet,
  Text,
  View
} from 'react-native';

import { gyroscope, setUpdateIntervalForType,
SensorTypes } from "react-native-sensors";

const Value = ({name, value}) => (
  <View style={styles.valueContainer}>
    <Text style={styles.valueName}>{name}:</Text>
    <Text style={styles.valueValue}>{new String(value).
substr(0, 8)}</Text>
  </View>
)

export default class GyroscopeScreen extends Component {
  constructor(props) {
    super(props);
    this.state = {
        x: 0,
        y: 0,
        z: 0,
        timestamp: 0,
    };
  }

  componentDidMount(){
    setUpdateIntervalForType(SensorTypes.gyroscope,
100);
```

```
     const subscription = gyroscope.subscribe(({ x, y, z,
timestamp }) =>
        this.setState({ x, y, z, timestamp })
     // This line will set the x, y, z, timestamp
values to the state        also we can send these
values to the ros server via web socket protocol.
   );
 }

  render() {
    return (
      <View style={styles.container}>
        <Text style={styles.headline}>
          Gyroscope values
        </Text>
        <Value name="x" value={this.state.x} />
        <Value name="y" value={this.state.y} />
        <Value name="z" value={this.state.z} />
      </View>
    );
  }
}

const styles = StyleSheet.create({
  container: {
    flex: 1,
    justifyContent: 'center',
    alignItems: 'center',
    backgroundColor: '#F5FCFF',
  },
  headline: {
    fontSize: 30,
    textAlign: 'center',
    margin: 10,
  },
  valueContainer: {
```

```
      flexDirection: 'row',
      flexWrap: 'wrap',
    },
    valueValue: {
      width: 200,
      fontSize: 20
    },
    valueName: {
      width: 50,
      fontSize: 20,
      fontWeight: 'bold'
    },
    instructions: {
      textAlign: 'center',
      color: '#333333',
      marginBottom: 5,
    },
});
```

The preceding code captures the gyroscope values from the device and displays them as shown in the following figure:

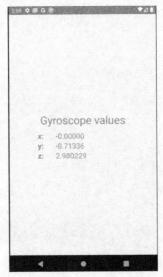

Figure 14.2: Screenshot of gyroscope values

Magnetometer values are used to aid in capturing the orientation of the robot. The sensor values from the device can be captured and displayed on the screen using the sample code shown here:

MagnetometerScreen.js

```javascript
import React, { Component } from 'react';
import {
  StyleSheet,
  Text,
  View
} from 'react-native';

import { magnetometer, setUpdateIntervalForType,
SensorTypes } from "react-native-sensors";

const Value = ({name, value}) => (
  <View style={styles.valueContainer}>
    <Text style={styles.valueName}>{name}:</Text>
    <Text style={styles.valueValue}>{new String(value).
substr(0, 8)}</Text>
  </View>
)

export default class MagnetometerScreen extends
Component {
  constructor(props) {
    super(props);
    this.state = {
        x: 0,
        y: 0,
        z: 0,
        timestamp: 0,
    };
  }

  componentDidMount(){
    setUpdateIntervalForType(SensorTypes.magnetometer,
100);
```

```
    const subscription = magnetometer.subscribe(({ x, y,
z, timestamp }) =>
        this.setState({ x, y, z, timestamp })
      // This line will set the x, y, z, timestamp
values to the state        also we can send these
values to the ros server via web socket protocol.
    );
  }

  render() {
    return (
      <View style={styles.container}>
        <Text style={styles.headline}>
          Magnetometer values
        </Text>
        <Value name="x" value={this.state.x} />
        <Value name="y" value={this.state.y} />
        <Value name="z" value={this.state.z} />
      </View>
    );
  }
}

const styles = StyleSheet.create({
  container: {
    flex: 1,
    justifyContent: 'center',
    alignItems: 'center',
    backgroundColor: '#F5FCFF',
  },
  headline: {
    fontSize: 30,
    textAlign: 'center',
    margin: 10,
  },
  valueContainer: {
```

```
      flexDirection: 'row',
      flexWrap: 'wrap',
    },
    valueValue: {
      width: 200,
      fontSize: 20
    },
    valueName: {
      width: 50,
      fontSize: 20,
      fontWeight: 'bold'
    },
    instructions: {
      textAlign: 'center',
      color: '#333333',
      marginBottom: 5,
    },
});
```

The magnetometer values captured from the device are shown on the screen as follows:

Figure 14.3: Screenshot of magnetometer values

Establishing the connection between the ROS server and React Native app

React Native supports WebSocket's, a protocol that provides full-duplex communication channels over a single TCP connection. The following code snippet helps in establishing a webscoket connection.

```
var ws = new WebSocket('ws://host.com/path');

ws.onopen = () => {
  // connection opened
ws.send('something'); // send a message
};

ws.onmessage = (e) => {
  // a message was received
  console.log(e.data);
};

ws.onerror = (e) => {
  // an error occurred
  console.log(e.message);
};

ws.onclose = (e) => {
  // connection closed
console.log(e.code, e.reason);
};
```

Connection with Non-ROS programs

Non-ROS programs can be defined as the set of software or custom codes that do not necessarily use the ros client libraries. This includes web apps, android applications, and other interfaces. In order to connect these interfaces with a robot, the ROS community provides a certain set of packages called the ROS bridge suite. As the name suggests, it acts as a bridge between a ROS network and a non-ROS program.

Functioning

ROS bridge suite provides the JSON API, which can be used to access ROS functionalities. Any program that can use or send JSON format will be able to use the ROS bridge. JSON stands for JavaScript Object Notation. The data exchanged between a server and browser should be text. JSON helps convert all the data into meaningful text without complicated syntax. JSON helps in faster communication and parsing and is widely compatible with most browsers and operating systems.

ROS bridge protocol

The rosbridge protocol describes the syntax or specification for the JSON commands to be sent to the rosbridge server. At a higher level, the commands are categorized into three fields:

- The operation to be performed
- Topic name
- Message type
- Message

The operation to be performed determines whether the non-ROS program subscribes or publishes to a topic. The topic name determines the topic under which the data should be published (if Publisher) or the topic to listen to, to get the required data (if subscriber). Here is an example of the JSON format:

```
{
"op": "subscribe",
        "topic": "/listener",
         "type": "std_msgs/String"
}
```

Transport layer

Transport layer is the term used in networking to describe the layer that is responsible for end-to-end communication across a network. The transport layer is the fourth layer in a seven-layered OSI model. To give a perspective about the transport layers, here are some examples: TCP and UDP.

ROS bridge uses the WebSocket protocol for end-to-end communication. Websocket helps build a full-duplex communication channel over a TCP connection. Once the connection is established, the JSON data is sent over to the ros bridge server. Websocket support is widely available and can be programmed using C++, Python, PHP, and JavaScript.

ROS bridge suite

The ROS bridge suite is a package available to establish a connection between a non-ROS program and the ROS network. The package includes three components:

- **ROS bridge server**: The ROS bridge server is a WebSocket server that acts as a link between the browser/other applications and the ROS network. The Websocket server is launched by default on port 9090. The port can be changed as per the requirement using a launch file.

- **ROS bridge library**: The ROS bridge library is responsible for converting JSON data into ROS commands and vice versa.

- **Rosapi**: The rosapi makes all the ros actions available to the ros bridge clients. These include actions like setting the parameter server values, calling for list of topics, etc.

Installation of ROS bridge suite

Open a terminal on Ubuntu and use the following command:

```
sudo apt-get install ros-kinetic-rosbridge-server
```

(Replace kinetic with the corresponding ROS version.)

Creating an application

In this section, we will build an application that will get the IMU values from a cell phone and publish it to an ROS topic. Publishing on a topic includes two steps:

- Advertise
- Publish

The first message to be sent after establishing a websocket connection with the ros bridge server is as follows:

Advertise

```
{
"op":"advertise",
"id":"advertise:/imu_val:1",
"type":"sensor_msgs/Imu",
"topic":"/imu_val",
"Latch":false,
"Queue_size":10
}
```

The second step includes publishing the sensor values:

Publish

```
{
"op":"publish",
"id":"publish:/cmd_vel:2",
"topic":"/cmd_vel",
"Msg":
{
 "header": {
                    "frame_id" : "world"
                              },
              "orientation" : {
                          "x ": quaternionpose.x,
                        "y" :quaternionpose.y,
                         "z" :quaternionpose.z,
                        "w" :quaternionpose.w
                              },
        "angular_velocity" : {
                                  "x" :vbeta,
                                  "y" :vgamma,
                                  "z" :valpha,
                                  },
              "linear_acceleration" : {
                                  "x" : x,
                                  "y" : y,
```

```
                                    "z" : z,
                                    },
},
"latch":false
}
```

Once the above-mentioned JSON is stored in a variable, convert the JavaScript object into a string using **JSON.stringify()** and send the message over the WebSocket connection.

Let's see how this approach can be implemented in React Native. I am taking **AccelerometerScreen.js** code as an example; a similar approach can be implemented for magnetometer and gyroscope code snippets. The accelerometerscreen.js code has been modified to publish data on an ROS topic. The code can be found in the code repository under the section Practical-guide-to-build-int-robot/ Codewith the name **ros_accelerometerScreen.js**.

Conclusion

React Native is an exciting framework that enables web developers to create robust mobile applications using the JavaScript knowledge they already have. It offers faster mobile development and more efficient code sharing across iOS, Android, and the Web without sacrificing the end user's experience or application quality. The trade-off is that it's new and still a work in progress.

The next chapter will introduce you to the basics of artificial intelligence and its implementation. It will help you integrate AI models with ROS.

Key terms

- **React native framework**: It is a JavaScript-based app framework that allows you to build natively rendered apps for iOS and Android.

- **ROS bridge suite**: It is a collection of packages used to implement the ros bridge protocol using the websocket transport layer.

- **WebSocket**: It is a communication protocol built over a TCP connection that provides full duplex communication.

CHAPTER 15
Artificial Intelligence

Introduction

Well-constructed algorithms are the backbone of any successful software/product. To impart **Artificial Intelligence (AI)** to a system, one needs to properly design algorithms. When an algorithm is implemented using a coding language like Java, Python, R, Lisp, Prolog, or C++ in a machine, it creates a domain-specific illusion of intelligence in the machine. This intelligence makes them capable of performing tasks, which would normally require human understanding, perception, and use of intelligence. This intelligent system will predict which action needs to be performed based on the environment to maximize the chances of success.

Structure

We will cover the following topics in this chapter:

- Introduction to artificial intelligence and machine learning
- Integration of AI and ML packages into the ROS environment
- Overview of the concepts – Object Detection, CNN, YOLO

Objectives

By the end of this chapter, you will be able to develop an accurate customer object detection model using image processing and the power of neural networks. This can be used for object detection in robotics.

Purpose of AI

In simple words, all AI algorithms perform the same task of predicting outputs given unknown inputs, but the algorithm selection is data-driven.

A properly trained AI model will be able to perform some of the tasks performed by humans, including:

- Learning from given input data; for example, object detection, which is a supervised learning process

- Reasoning and self-learning; for example, learning association and relationships among large sets of data items

- Grouping from patterns; for example, pattern recognition used for product recommendations

- Planning and decision-making; for example, autonomous driving and pathfinding that involves reinforcement learning

Application of AI

The process flow for training an AI model is shown in *figure 15.1*. AI algorithms provide solutions to a wide variety of day-to-day problems. The problem statements in AI fall under the following three categories:

- Classification
- Regression
- Clustering

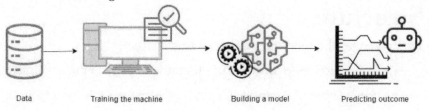

| Data | Training the machine | Building a model | Predicting outcome |

Figure 15.1: Machine learning process

Consider an online shopping scenario. The owner of the website has a few requirements: categorize the products, predict the quantity of products that would be purchased based on the usage statistics, and generate product recommendations based on the personal purchase details of customers. All these can be done with the help of AI. Let's see how.

To classify the products into categories (which are discrete values, so go for classification), the product description is pre-processed by converting the textual descriptions into numerical form. The resultant data set is used to train a model, which is built on classification algorithms like SVM or naive bayes. Now, to forecast the quantity of products (a continuous value, hence regression task), linear regression algorithm is used. Finally, K means clustering is done on the product list on the website, and products belonging to the same group are identified and recommended to the buyers based on their purchase history.

Widely used machine learning algorithms are shown in *figure 15.2*:

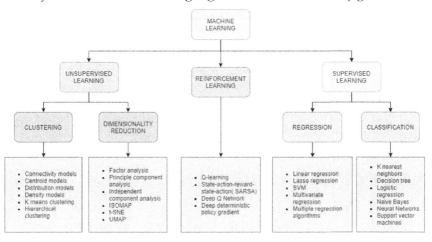

Figure 15.2: Machine learning algorithms

Choosing between machine learning and deep learning

Machine Learning (**ML**) and **Deep Learning** (**DL**) are two common approaches that one comes across while learning about AI. These are the subsets of AI. A problem can be solved either using ML or

DL algorithm, depending on the amount and type of data used for training and based on the complexity of the features.

Table 15.1 gives an idea about choosing the approach for solving a problem:

Criterion	Machine Learning	Deep Learning
Size of training dataset	Small	Large and diverse
Feature engineering	Derive features manually	Network calculates features
Training time	Few minutes to hours	Days to weeks
Hardware dependency	Low-end machine	High-end machine, preferably GPU

Table 15.1: Machine learning vs deep learning [2]

Of late, DL is used predominantly in robotic solutions where it is combined with advanced vision systems. In the field of robotics, an AI algorithm can help achieve tasks like real-time course correction, object detection, face recognition, position estimation, **Optical Character Recognition** (**OCR**), voice recognition, speech synthesis, natural language understanding, and natural language generation. In this chapter, we will discuss the AI algorithm for object detection and its implementation in robotics.

Object detection

Object detection in the context of image processing and AI is defined as the process of identifying or recognizing an object or item of interest in a scene or image, along with its location in the scene or image. For videos, object detection is generally combined with an object tracking algorithm to ensure the continuity of the identified objects across multiple scenes. The choice of object detection algorithm varies based on the objective of the use case. Based on this, the type of image annotation techniques also varies from common box type or polygonal annotation to segmentation masks and superpixel annotations. Before understanding object detection in detail, let's take a look at some basic aspects related to it.

Understanding computer vision

Computer vision helps with image processing tasks in AI. When combined with suitable AI algorithms, it gives robots the capability to make sense out of the vision captured by its camera. It makes the robot useful in domains like **safety**, **security**, **health**, **access**, and **entertainment**. OpenCV helps with everyday tasks like object avoidance in case of autonomous driving, and it detects suspicious activities on camera feed and helps thwart crimes. It also performs minimally invasive surgeries and provide access based on face recognition. Plus, it comes in handy in the infotainment sector for content generation, marketing, and personalization.

Computer vision performs automatic extraction and analysis of information from one image or an array of images (in case of videos). However, it requires combining the capabilities of computer vision with suitable algorithms for imparting intelligence to the robot.

For any computer vision system to be used in a hardware setup, it requires power supply; image acquisition devices such as camera, processor, software, display device, etc. for monitoring the system; and other accessories.

Tasks of computer vision

The different activities involved in computer vision algorithms are as follows:

- **OCR**: It is a software used to read printed characters, including alphabets and numbers, from documents.

- **Face detection**: Face detection algorithms in AI are used for face authentication, recognition, counting the number of people in front of the camera, etc.

- **Object recognition**: Object recognition algorithms are installed in supermarkets, cameras, and high-end cars of BMW, GM, and Volvo for recognizing objects.

- **Estimating position**: It involves determining the location of an object with respect to the camera, for example, locating a tumor in a person's body.

Object detection – An explanation

As discussed, earlier, object detection aims to identify the type of objects inside an image with its relative location. For any object detection task, the object is defined by the user. For example, if the camera in front of a car is required to detect all cars and people in the vicinity, the 'objects of interest' will be cars and people. First, the images of these objects need to be collected. Then, a suitable algorithm for object detection needs to be identified.

The model architecture for object detection can either be developed from the beginning or a transfer learning approach can be used; training is performed on specific class of objects on a pre-existing model architecture. From an image input, the algorithm outputs a list of objects, each associated with a class label and its location (usually in the form of bounding box coordinates). In practice, only limited types of 'objects of interests' are considered, and the rest of the image is recognized as object-less background.

Figure 15.3 shows the objection detection performed on the road:

Figure 15.3: *Objects detected on a road*

When an image is seen, the human brain instantly recognizes the objects in it, the location of the objects, and even an approximate field of depth. On the other hand, it takes a lot of time and tremendous amount of training data for a machine to undertake such seemingly easy tasks, including identifying the objects. The machine learns by studying the features of tens of thousands of different images of an object until it can decide with the highest accuracy that the observed image is of a particular object. With recent advances in hardware and DL, the process of object detection is simplified.

To teach the machine to recognize objects, the image of the object to be detected is passed to our algorithm so that the algorithm learns the features of the image, like edges, shapes, color, position, textures, objects, etc. However, the ML approach has one shortcoming: the features relevant to the object need to be manually extracted. On the other hand, in the DL approach, the features of the images are extracted by the network itself.

Figure 15.4 shows an example of how a **neural network** (**NN**) perceives the features of an object:

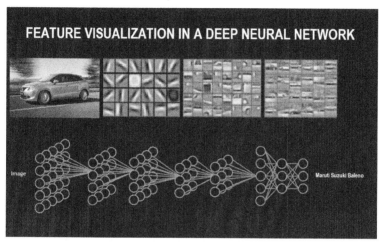

Figure 15.4: *Feature extraction by NN*

It is a desirable feature for a robot to recognize the objects in front of it for decisions regarding movement. If the robot identifies a hazardous object, it can move backward or raise an alarm. It is also interesting to get the robot to greet a person in front of it as Mr. or Ms. based on the gender. It will be more interesting if it could recognize the person and address them by name.

Object detection methods used in robots can be classified mainly on the basis of the following:

- How they recognize objects

- The amount of time they take to understand an image

The methods used for object detection are the following:

- **Boosted cascade classifiers**: Also called Coarse-to-Fine classifiers, they work by defining a set of filters to evaluate image segments. The, they eliminate image segments that do not match a predefined object. The efficiency achieved with this approach is high.

- **Dictionary-based object detection algorithms**: These algorithms check for the presence or absence of a specific object in an image, giving them higher priority over other unknown objects in the background. They can also be used to detect the co-occurrence of more than one classes of objects in an image.

- **Partial object handling**: In this approach, every object is described as a set of parts that can be measured. The descriptors of these parts may use oriented gradients. Partial object handling, when used along with boosted cascade classifiers, speeds up the object detection process.

- **Convolutional neural network (CNN)**: This is a widely used object detection method these days. This algorithm allows the model to learn the objects' features and classify the objects based on the values of the features present rather than following a rule-based programmatic approach for object detection or classification. In this chapter, we will discuss the CNN approach. In CNNs, the features extracted from the images are passed as input into the algorithms in order to recognize instances of an object category.

- **Structured algorithms**: Each module is dedicated to a different kind of detected item: module for objects, module for features, module for text, and so on. Each of the module's parameters are set by training.

Working of CNN

Before learning the working of object detection algorithms, one should have a basic understanding of image representation in computers. So, let's see how CNN (or ConvNets) form the basic building blocks for the computer vision tasks in DL. CNNs form the base of object detection or any image processing task involving neural network.

Architecture of CNN

The algorithm that is used will detect the pattern in the image and decide what type of object is there in the image. This is achieved by using CNN, which is a type of deep neural network most frequently used for image-based and visual tasks in DL. A visual representation of CNN architecture is shown in *figure 15.5*.

CNNs use only a few pre-processing steps, and the network learns the filters that were designed manually in traditional algorithms.

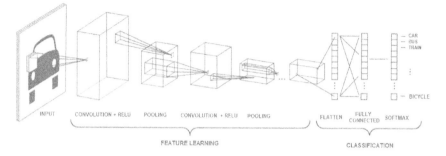

Figure 15.5: *Convolutional neural network*

The CNN consists of the following:

- Input layer
- Hidden layers (one or more)
- Output layer

The hidden layers consist of the following:

- Convolutional layers
- RELU function (activation function)
- Pooling layers
- Fully-connected layers
- Normalization layers

During training and testing, each input image passes through these layers. Then, a Softmax function is applied at the output of the fully-connected layer to classify an object with probabilistic values between 0 and 1.

Convolution layer

Convolution is the first layer of a CNN architecture, and the function of this layer is to extract features from an input image. Convolution learns image features using small squares of input data.

It is a mathematical operation between two matrices to give a third matrix. The smaller matrix, which is called filter or kernel, is operated on the matrix of image pixels. Depending on the numbers in the filter matrix, the output matrix recognizes specific patterns in the input image.

Refer to *figure 15.6* to understand how two-dimensional convolution is performed on images:

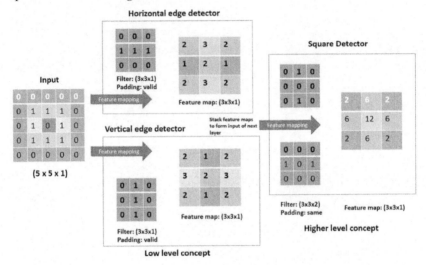

Figure 15.6: Two-dimensional convolution

For example, a filter, which is a vertical edge detector, learns vertical edges in the input image. In CNNs, the input images and their subsequent outputs are passed through several such filters. The network learns the number of filters and the patterns are derived on its own. The process of feature map generation from the input images is shown in *figure 15.7*:

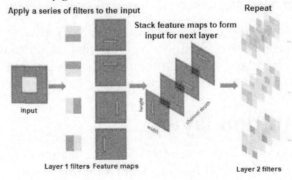

Figure 15.7: Feature map generation

ReLU

Since the images are non-linear in real world, a method is required to impose non-linearity to the network. The **rectified linear unit (ReLU)** layer applies an activation function onto our feature maps to increase the non-linearity in the network. This operation removes negative values from an activation map by making them zero. Although activation functions like tanh and sigmoid are available, ReLU is used widely because it leads to faster training without compromising on accuracy.

Padding

At times, the filter may not fit the input image perfectly. There are two solutions to this problem:

- **Zero-padding**: Pad the picture with zeros so that it fits.

- **Valid padding**: Drop part of the image where the filter did not fit.

Pooling

Pooling layers reduces the dimensions of the data. It combines the outputs of neuron clusters at one layer into a single neuron in the next layer. A visualization of pooling can be seen in *figure 15.8*:

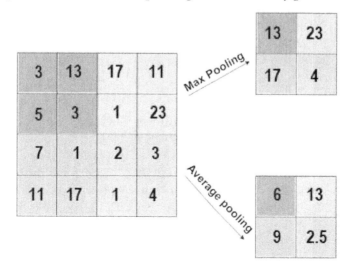

Figure 15.8: Max pooling

Pooling can be used to reduce the number of parameters when the images are too large. It also reduces the computational complexity and prevents overfitting. Spatial pooling (subsampling or down sampling) reduces the dimensionality of each map and retains only the important information. Spatial pooling can be of different types:

- **Max pooling**: Uses the maximum value from the cluster of neurons of the previous layer.

- **Average pooling**: Uses the average value from each cluster of neurons of the previous layer.

- **Sum pooling**: Uses the sum value from each cluster of neurons of the previous layer.

Flattening

The flattening layer converts the data output from convolutional layers into a one-dimensional array (a single long feature vector) for inputting it to the next layer.

Fully connected layer

Fully connected (**FC**) layers connect each neuron in one layer to each neuron in the next layer. The convolution layers previously occurring in the architecture, before the FC layer(s), contain the information regarding local features in the input image, such as edges, shapes, corners, etc. The FC layer holds the aggregated information from all the convolution layers. The flattening layer converts the processed data into the form of a one-dimensional linear vector. This output of flattening goes through the FC layer to classify the images.

Softmax layer

Softmax function assigns probabilities to each class in a multi-class problem. Since the outputs of a Softmax function can be interpreted as a probability (they must sum to 1), a Softmax layer is typically the final layer used in NN functions. It is important to note that a Softmax layer must have the same number of nodes as the output later.

There are two types of Softmax:

- **Full Softmax**: It calculates a probability for every possible class.

- **Candidate sampling**: It calculates a probability for all the positive labels but only for a random sample of negative labels. For example, to determine whether an input image is audi A7 or a volvo 360, it is not necessary to provide probabilities for every non-car example.

Weights

The weights of a neural network are initialized to random values. Each neural network learns a function that best describes the desired output from the input values. The output of the neural network is computed by applying this function to input values. This function is specified by a vector of weights and a bias (typically, real numbers). Learning in a neural network happens by making incremental adjustments to the biases and weights. Each feature of the input, for example, a shape, is represented by a vector of weights and biases, which is also called 'filter'. In CNNs, many neurons share the same filter. This helps reduce memory footprint because a single bias and a single vector of weights is used across all receptive fields sharing that filter.

Object detection using CNN

The algorithms available for object detection are as follows:

- RCNN
- YOLO
- SSD

1. **RCNN – Region-based convolutional neural network**

   The RCNN family consists of RCNN, fast RCNN, faster RCNN, and mask RCNN.

   i) **RCNN:** RCNN extracts a set of regions from the given image using an approach called selective search. It checks if any of these boxes contains an object. Each of this region is extracted, and CNN is used to extract specific features for each region. Finally, these features are used to detect objects. The entire process involves three separate models:

      - CNN for image classification and feature extraction

- The top SVM classifier for identifying the target objects

- The regression model for tightening region bounding boxes

Figure 15.9 shows RCNN components:

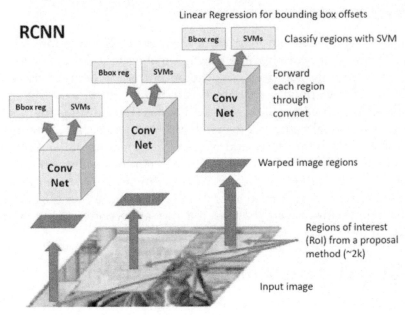

Figure 15.9: RCNN architecture

RCNN becomes slow due to multiple steps involved in the process.

ii) **Fast RCNN:** Fast RCNN passes the entire image to ConvNet, which generates regions of interest (instead of passing the extracted regions from the image). Instead of using three different models as in RCNN, it uses a single model. This model does the following things:

- It extracts features from the regions.

- It classifies them into different classes.

- It returns the bounding boxes.

Figure 15.10: shows how fast RCNN works:

Fast R-CNN

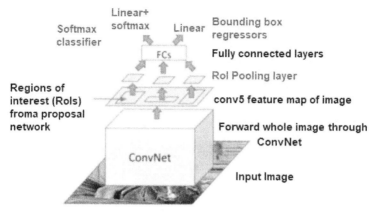

Figure 15.10: Fast RCNN architecture

It is fast when compared to RCNN, and it also uses selective search for extracting the regions.

iii) **Faster RCNN:** Faster RCNN fixes the problem of selective search by replacing it with **Region Proposal Network (RPN)**. Here, the feature maps are extracted from the input image using ConvNet and then passed through RPN, which returns object proposals. Finally, these maps are classified, and the bounding boxes are predicted. Refer to *figure 15.11*:

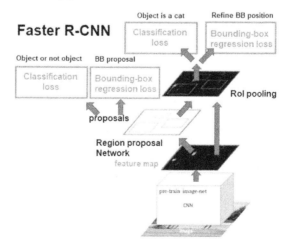

Figure 15.11: Faster RCNN architecture

iv) **Mask RCNN:** Mask RCNN extends faster RCNN to pixel-level image segmentation. Here, the classification and the pixel-level mask prediction tasks are decoupled. It added a third branch for predicting an object mask parallelly with the existing branches for classification and localization. The third branch called mask branch is a fully connected network applied to each **region of interest (RoI)**, which is used for predicting a segmentation mask in a pixel-to-pixel manner. This helps in mapping RoI to the regions of the original image precisely.

Mask RCNN can be understood better from the architecture in *figure 15.12*:

Mask R-CNN

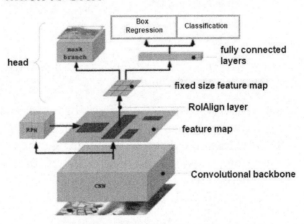

Figure 15.12: Mask RCNN architecture

2. YOLO-You only look once

This network, instead of looking at the entire image, looks at the parts of the images that have higher chances of containing an object.

Compared to fast RCNNs, which perform detection on various region proposals and thus, perform prediction multiple times for various regions in an image, YOLO architecture is more like the **fully convolutional neural network (FCNN)**. It passes the image (nxn) once through the FCNN, and the output is the (mxm) prediction. This architecture splits the input image in mxm grid and for each grid generation, two bounding boxes and class probabilities for those bounding boxes are given as output. The architecture of YOLO is shown in *figure 15.13*:

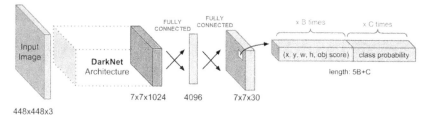

Figure 15.13: YOLO architecture

The following steps are involved in YOLO object detection:

1. Takes input image.
2. Divides the image into grids.
3. Performs image classification.
4. Localization is applied on each grid.
5. YOLO predicts the bounding boxes and their corresponding class probabilities for objects.

YOLO is faster than other object detection algorithms, but due to spatial constraints, it has trouble detecting small objects within the image.

3. SSD – Single shot detector

SSD is designed for object detection in real-time. SSD does not have region proposal network; hence, it is faster. To overcome the reduced accuracy, SSD applies multi-scale features and default boxes. Based on comparison with other object detection algorithms discussed above, it achieves the real-time processing speed and even beats the accuracy of faster RCNN.

The architecture of SSD can be seen in *figure 15.14*:

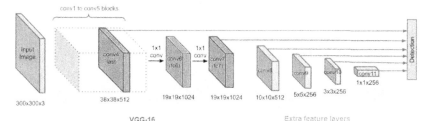

Figure 15.14: SSD architecture

Coding exercise

Let's revise the concepts mentioned in the earlier sections using code.

Object detection using Tensorflow object detection API

The TensorFlow Object Detection API is an open-source framework built on top of TensorFlow. It can be used for constructing, training, and deploying object detection models.

Now, we will look at how to select a model, adapt to an existing data set, create and annotate an own data set, modify the model configuration file, train the model, save the model, and finally, deploy the model in another piece of software.

You can refer to this instruction manual for the following:

- Installing Tensorflow
- Installing Tensorflow models
- Installing labelImg
- Training custom object detector

https://buildmedia.readthedocs.org/media/pdf/tensorflow-object-detection-api-tutorial/latest/tensorflow-object-detection-api-tutorial.pdf

After following the instructions in the above-mentioned PDF, a custom model is generated. The following code shows how this trained model can be used for detecting objects in live camera feed:

```
1.  import numpy as np
2.  import os
3.  import six.moves.urllib as urllib
4.  import sys
5.  import tarfile
6.  import tensorflow as tf
7.  import zipfile
8.  from collections, import defaultdict
9.  from io import StringIO
10. from matplotlib import pyplot as plt
```

```
11. from PIL import Image
12. import cv2
13. from utils import label_map_util
14. from utils import visualization_utils as vis_util
15. cap = cv2.VideoCapture(0)
16. sys.path.append("..")
17. # What model to download.
18. MODEL_NAME = 'custom_model'
19. # Path to frozen detection graph. This is the
    actual model that is used for the object detection.
20. PATH_TO_CKPT = 'trained-inference-graphs/output_
    inference_graph_v1.pb'
21. # List of the strings that is used to add correct
    label for each box.
22. PATH_TO_LABELS = 'training_demo/annotations/label_
    map.pbtxt')
23. NUM_CLASSES = 90
24. detection_graph = tf.Graph()
25. with detection_graph.as_default():
26. od_graph_def = tf.GraphDef()
27.         with tf.gfile.GFile(PATH_TO_CKPT, 'rb') as
    fid:
28. serialized_graph = fid.read()
29. od_graph_def.ParseFromString(serialized_graph)
30. tf.import_graph_def(od_graph_def, name='')
31. label_map = label_map_util.load_labelmap(PATH_TO_
    LABELS)
32. categories = label_map_util.convert_label_map_to_
    categories(label_map,
33. max_num_classes=NUM_CLASSES, use_display_name=True)
34. category_index = label_map_util.create_category_
    index(categories)
35. with detection_graph.as_default():
36.         with tf.Session(graph=detection_graph) as
    sess:
37.                 while True:
```

```
38.                        ret, image_np = cap.read()
39.                        # Expand dimensions since the
    model expects images to have shape: [1, None, None, 3]
40. image_np_expanded = np.expand_dims(image_np,
    axis=0)
41. image_tensor = detection_graph.get_tensor_by_
    name('image_tensor:0')
42.                        # Each box represents a
    part of the image where a particular object was
    detected.
43.                        boxes = detection_graph.
    get_tensor_by_name('detection_boxes:0')
44.                        # Each score represents how
    Level of confidence for each of the objects.
45.                        # Score is shown on the
    result image, together with the class Label.
46.                        scores = detection_graph.
    get_tensor_by_name('detection_scores:0')
47.                        classes = detection_graph.
    get_tensor_by_name('detection_classes:0')
48. num_detections = detection_graph.get_tensor_by_
    name('num_detections:0')
49.                        # Actual detection.
50.                        (boxes, scores, classes,
    num_detections) = sess.run(
51.                            [boxes, scores,
    classes, num_detections],
52. feed_dict={image_tensor: image_np_expanded})
53.                        # Visualization of the
    results of a detection.
54. vis_util.visualize_boxes_and_labels_on_image_array(7
55. image_np,
56. np.squeeze(boxes),
57. np.squeeze(classes).astype(np.int32),
58. np.squeeze(scores),
59. category_index,
60. use_normalized_coordinates=True,
```

```
61. line_thickness=8)
62. cv2.imshow('object detection', cv2.resize(image_np,
    (800,600)))
63. if cv2.waitKey(25) 0xFF == ord('q'):
64.         cv2.destroyAllWindows()
65.         break
```

The preceding code must have helped you gain a good understanding of how object detection is performed from a trained custom model.

Let's look at the various parts of the code to understand it better. Steps 1 to 13 show the import of necessary libraries. Step 14 initializes video capture. In steps 17 to 22, the model details are specified. At step 23, a Tensorflow graph is initialized. Graph is an abstract concept, which can be in different forms for different frontends. For Python, **tf.Graph()** would return a Python object (code) that contains the GraphDef and many utilities. To run a graph loaded from the protobuf file (. pb), one should use a GraphDef and bind the GraphDef to a (default) Graph and then use a session to run the Graph for computation. Steps 24 to 29 deal with using GraphDef and binding it to a Graph.

Steps 30 to 33 show creating categories and indexing them. At step 35, a Tensorflow session is started. At step 37, each frame of video is captured; at 39, the shape of array is expanded; at 40, an image tensor is created; and at 42, boxes that represent a particular object detected are identified. At 45, we calculate the level of confidence of each object. At 46, the classes are identified, and at 47, the number of detections in the image is identified. At 49, boxes, scores, classes, num_detections are calculated by feeding the image tensor to the placeholder. At 51, the image with the identified boxes is visualized, along with the class to which each boxed object belongs, the accuracy of prediction, and the category index. At 52, the image is shown. From 53 to 55, the code for closing the video window by pressing the 'q' key is written.

Tensorflow object detection with ROS

The code for the given experiment is provided at the following GitHub link:

> < Code/Chapter 15 at master · Practical-guide-to-build-int-robot/ Code (github.com)>

Requirements

The basic software requirements for the given experiment are as follows:

- Tensorflow and ROS
- Ubuntu 16.04 and ROS Kinetic

Steps

Follow these steps to run the default SSD algorithm :

1. Install ROS: **http://wiki.ros.org/kinetic/Installation/Ubuntu**.

2. Install camera dependencies:

    - `sudo apt-get install ros-kinetic-usb_cam ros-kinetic-openni2-launch`

3. Install tensorflow into python virtualenv: **https://www.tensorflow.org/install/install_linux**.

    - `sudo apt-get install python-pip python-dev python-virtualenv`

    - `virtualenv --system-site-packages ~/tensorflow`

    - `source ~/tensorflow/bin/activate`

    - `easy_install -U pip`

    - `pip install --upgrade tensorflow`

4. mkdir ~/catkin_ws/ &&mkdir ~/catkin_ws/src/

5. Clone or Copy the standard Vision messages repository from GitHub (link given in the instructions below) and the code repository for *Chapter 15, "Artificial Intelligence"* of this book into **catkin_ws/src** folder::

    - `cd ~/catkin_ws/src`

    - `git clone https://github.com/Kukanani/vision_msgs.git`

    - `git clone to the github repository of code` of *Chapter 15, "Artificial Intelligence"* of this book.

6. Build tensorflow_object_detector and Vision message:

    - `cd ~/catkin_ws&&catkin_make`

7. Source catkin workspace's by running the following command:

    *   `source ~/catkin_ws/devel/setup.bash`

8. Plug in camera and launch Single Shot Detector (varies per camera; **note:** object_detect.launch also launches the openni2. launch file for the camera. In case any other camera is being used, change the camera topic in the launch file before launching the file):

    *   `roslaunchtensorflow_object_detectorobject_detect. launch`

                              OR

    *   `roslaunchtensorflow_object_detectorusb_cam_ detector.launch`

Follow the given steps to try any other ML model:

1. Download any object detection models from the Tensorflow Object Detection API and place it in **data/models/**. You can find the models in Tensorflow Object Detection Model Zoo at **https://github.com/tensorflow/models/blob/master/object_ detection/g3doc/detection_model_zoo.md**. Then, extract the **tar.gz** file.

2. Edit the MODEL_NAME and LABEL_NAME in detect_ros. py. By default, they are ssd_mobilenet_v1_coco_11_06_2017 and **mscoco_label_map.pbtxt**, respectively.

3. For custom object detection, replace the model name with the new model name and change **label.pbtxt** accordingly.

Conclusion

Object detection is a necessary skill for a robot to perform tasks in human-involved environments. This chapter took you through the basics of AI, computer vision, CNN algorithm, and Tensorflow object detection in detail. This chapter also discussed in detail how to use image processing and the power of neural networks to develop an accurate custom object detection model, which can be used in robotics for object detection, making navigation possible through space.

Key terms

- **Object detection**: It is a computer vision technique that helps us to identify and locate objects in an image or video.

- **CNN:** Convolutional neural network or CNN is a deep learning algorithm that is used to analyze visual images by processing data with grid like topology.

- **Tensorflow:** It is google's open source AI framework for machine learning and high performance numerical computation.

The book walked you through the journey of making a practical and intelligent robot from scratch. Starting from the basics of the Robotics operating system, we moved ahead and learned complex topics through easily understandable steps and real-world examples of implementation. Toward the end, we implemented AI-driven intelligent modeling to enhance the value of our robotic solution.

We believe that the book showed justice to its purpose of helping a beginner to easily build their first intelligent robot in the shortest timespan with expert advice from a team that develops and implements robots, AI, and mobility-based solutions as part of their passion.

Index